THE REUNION

Coming of Age in the Age of Aquarius

GARY WELLS

Contents

"A Boy Named Sue"

Nicknames can be funny, but not the one a bully gave Nick. As he thinks about what to say if that classmate uses that name, Nick recalls the still legendary party at his house where he took control of events and kept the bully and everyone else out of trouble.

"Chain of Fools"

The appetizer table is a perfect place for an introvert to talk to people. You can't hold up the line for long. Nick pegs classmates there for a Thrillist story on "10 People You See at Your High School Reunion." But he discovers he actually wants to see some of them.

"Light My Fire"

One reason Nick had a lot of friends who were girls was they thought he listened. He just never knew what to say to any girl. And when he finally decided to confront THAT girl in the spring of 1967, he turned the Summer of Love into a Nuclear Winter.

"Glory Days"

Nick is cadged into a group telling stories. Why do we talk so much about what we did when we were kids? Maybe, he thinks, it's to remind us that we really were young. We did a lot of stupid shit growing up in the Sixties. It seemed like a good idea at the time.

"Something in the Air"

His friend the ski coach announces he is hooking up with his lost love. Then he presses Nick to explain how and why he and THAT girl broke up. What if, Nick begins his story, you make what could have been the biggest mistake of your life, when you're 19.

"Things I'd Like to Say"

Nick trounces his friend in naming songs on the playlist. Dinner, the reunion chief says, in ten minutes. THAT girl isn't here. What, Nick wonders, would anyone say to their first love? Would you have the courage, if you had the chance? He is about to find out.

"Still Crazy After All These Years"

When Nick goes home, his wife asks if his friend the ski coach was there. And THAT girl. Exhausted as introverts always are after talking to many people, Nick recalls what his father once said: "Preserve your memories ... they're all that's left you."

"You Were On My Mind"
                    —*We Five*

"Who Knows Where the Time Goes"
                    —*Fairport Convention*

"I Remember Everything"
                    —*John Prine*

Note from the Author

This book is dedicated to everyone who lived through the era - and to those who may be curious about the Sixties. There was, as everybody knows, sex, drugs, music, war and protests.

But that is only part of the story. There was also life to live.

This is a work of fiction. Any resemblance to persons alive or not is … unfortunate. Hey, get over it.

Acknowledgements

I would like to thank Sasha Bogin of Toronto for her book edits, Allison Barnhart of Ashland, Ohio, for her cover designs and Lorna Reid of Glasgow for her interior designs.

Also, Sarah Wells, a published author with more books coming soon, for her developmental edits and review of design concepts; Rhonda Wells and Herb Hutchison for reading the first draft and offering keen insights toward the final draft; Sarah, Rhonda and Mark Buie for reviewing designs and offering suggestions; Kerry Miller, for reading the draft and offering suggestions but mostly, despite being far away, for being a friend since those days long ago; and the McPherson Family, for their kindness and acceptance when it was needed.

Chapter 1

"Just Dropped In (To See What Condition My Condition Was In)"

Jerry Richards.

I really hated *Howdy Doody*.

Jerry Richards stands in the doorway, pretty much like everyone else when they arrive at this 50th reunion of the last high school class to graduate in the Sixties—the class of 1969—and sweeps the room.

Jerry and I were best friends when we were five. By six, it was over. All because of *Howdy Doody*.

He sees me standing at a tall table by the bar. I nod. He nods. But he might not recognize me at all—not unusual as so few classmates do. He might be nodding just because I nodded.

I hope Jerry looks elsewhere, and he does.

Howdy Doody ran every Saturday. Jerry wouldn't even contemplate playing outside until the show was over.

I thought *Howdy Doody*—the character and the show—was just flat-out stupid.

"Say kids, what time is it?" I can still hear that opening line and the sappy response: *"It's Howwwwwwwwww-deeeee Doody time!"*

Yeah. Time for me to go outside and play.

If all the other kids in the neighborhood watched *Howdy Doody* and Buffalo Bob, I could still find something to do. When you're an only kid, you learn how to entertain yourself. It's that or die of boredom and ennui.

One of my chores was to hose down the concrete back porch that ran the length of the house, a ranch. I always reenacted a battle, using the water spray, for example, to cut off the retreat of the German Sixth Army at Stalingrad …

Wonder how many other kids played Zhukov versus Von Paulus when they did their chores? … hmmm …. Yet another random thought … if there is a series of random thoughts that pop up in your mind, can they really be random?

STOP IT.

Random thoughts … random thoughts ….

Tonight is one of those times when random thoughts seem to come at me faster than normal, triggered by a glance or a face sending me to places forever locked in a faultless memory.

Trigger … why would Roy Rogers name his horse …

The memories attached to those faces are not a surprise. If you spend your entire formative years in the same school then you will have spent a dozen years with your classmates.

Even at our age, that is almost 20 percent of your life. Although I came to this school later, it still remains ten percent of my entire life.

But it isn't even just the random thoughts associated with these people. It's the neural associations those thoughts generate. Neural associations are the voices in my head—songs or scripts or facts for example—usually prompted by thoughts or events.

Like Jerry Richards and *Howdy Doody.*

Is it just me? Or is it everyone? Maybe nobody has voices in their heads. Maybe it is just those who are crazy.

Hey, now that *is a cheery thought.*

You can live in your imagination, but it is a dangerous place. Much like living in the past. Lotta traps there.

Being an only kid is dangerous, too. So much you do not know.

Random thoughts ... now I am stuck on Buffalo Bob.

The truth is that I liked Buffalo Bob. He wore a fringe jacket just like on the cowboy shows on television. Not as cool as, say, Davy Crockett and that coonskin cap. But then Buffalo Bob never pretended to be a cowboy. In fact, I'm pretty sure the name was derived from his hometown of Buffalo.

Yet I thought he must have been pretty smart to get a job on television. Actually, more because he came up with a gig that so many kids liked. Just not me.

Mighty Mouse was different. I did stay inside on Saturday mornings in the Fifties to watch the little mouse beat on big bullies. That really appealed to me.

Go figure.

Jerry and I never reconciled, even after his family followed mine from gritty, industrial Barberton where we started school to the suburbs growing outside the much larger, if also industrial, Akron.

Mercifully, Jerry finally moves out of my line of sight. I pretend to sip my beer and study the crowd.

Random thoughts ... random thoughts ....

Staying in my head keeps me from having to talk to people. Which makes me wonder, why do we go to class reunions? Especially if you don't really seem to want to talk to people. No matter how much of your life you spent with them.

It isn't that I won't talk to people. It's just that there are only certain people who really interest me. I haven't seen any of them just yet.

It's an introvert thing. You wouldn't understand.

Whenever I go to any gathering, I always try to be a little late. That way I can choose conversation partners from who are already there. This can be hard to do with my wife. She is the life of every party. People want to be with her because she is fun, she is hilarious.

Once, I went to a global conference in Buenos Aires. Usually the spouses attended, too. But this was spring 2002 and there were mass protests against the government, so she stayed home. When I arrived at the hotel where the conference was held, the host greeted me but said, "Where's your wife?" I said, "She's not coming." He said, nonplussed, "You mean it's just you?"

Yeah, it's just me. Sorry to disappoint everyone.

I am just quietly witty and charming. At least in my own mind.

But despite the strategy of getting here a little late, those people I care to talk with more than others, are not here. Where is Tom Baker? Pisses me off. I might actually have to talk to someone else.

Is this sort of like hanging out at Starbucks or what? Another random thought ….

I am afraid to look at anything but my beer. After all, I ration my words far more than my drinks. I do not drink much.

Most people from large families think I had it made, being an only kid. You get everything, they would tell me. Not really. And anyway, there are a lot of inherent downsides they never considered.

You don't know what's cool in music or clothes at any moment.

You don't know what's appropriate to say or not in any situation.

And you don't know how to talk to others.

Certainly not with girls. Some pretty girl would say hi and I would fall in love. No one ever talked to me. This had to mean she liked me. Right?

Like Susie Welker.

Susie Welker was a pretty, petite and shy strawberry blonde in the class ahead of mine. One day when I was a sophomore, we passed in the hall and she said hello. Shocked, I could only mumble, "Uh, hi," in reply.

Did that mean she liked me? It had to mean she liked me, right? Why else would she talk to *me*?

So I scoured the yearbooks for any information about her. And I casually asked others about her as well, and fended off all the inevitable questions on whether I liked her or not.

No, I said. She's just someone in one of my classes.

But I was sure prepared to like *her* if she liked *me*. In the end, she was just being polite. I wasn't crushed. I didn't even know her.

Except I had begun to wonder if news of our going steady would affect THAT girl—every guy had a THAT girl, and I guess every girl had a THAT guy, too—and how she looked at me.

In the end, it didn't matter. I don't think Susie Welker ever looked at me again. Or spoke to me, either.

I look quickly around the room. Nope, still nobody I want to spend a lot time talking to about whatever. What a snob.

Sesame Street *is brought to you today by the letters J, E, R, and K.*

Another random thought, but at least this one makes me smile: if you're smart—not always the case for me—you keep to yourself.

I was stupid, silly and goofy for a long time. Until I wasn't. Eventually, I learned how to converse easily with anyone. Being a reporter where it is your job to ask questions really helped. You just ask people about themselves. A good conversationalist is someone who lets you talk about yourself.

I glance around at my gathering classmates, and the question bobs to the surface again. Why do we go to class reunions?

"Come Together" by The Beatles pops into my head. Yeah, you know, I've always wondered if the sound the old rotary phones made, that staccato click click click, when the finger plate wheeled back to start . . . and you have to be of a certain age to know what that is . . . was that what John Lennon and Paul McCartney were thinking of when they conceived the distinctive drum riff for Ringo Starr to play on the toms in this song? Or did Ringo create it himself?

Geez, off track, much?

Is that really why we go to reunions? To come together? I love that song. My generation, and others, loved every Beatles song, but it is not playing on the sound system. It is only in my head. An answer to the question that fills my time.

We come together at reunions for a lot of reasons. Or not.

Look at me. I was voted second for the "shyest classmate." Nobody knew the kid who won. Or has seen him since.

Why *am* I here? I guess I am curious about why others are here. I think most people attend class reunions because classmates are people who knew you when ...

"I Knew You When" by Billy Joe Royal pops into my head. Of course it does. It's not as if I know every song that came out when I was a kid. Might have been one or two I never heard ... and I do know that Joe South wrote that particular song ....

STOP IT.

Classmates are people who knew you when you were growing up, hardly the wonder years, for most of us. So a common bond, a shared experience, or ... whatever. But there is generally an acceptance of each other. A lasting or perhaps blind trust in each other. For many, but not all, anyway.

Some people who were popular in school show up. Some who were never popular show up. Some people show up to demonstrate they're exactly who they were in school. Some show up to prove they're not. Some of them socialize with others, flitting from one person or group to another, to talk with as many classmates as possible. Some just sit at tables with their spouses or partners and talk or maybe not with others at their table.

As for me, I mobilize around a self-inflicted silence at a bar table.

Pretty sure we attend class reunions to remember being young. Why else would you go to a class reunion and not want to talk to anyone? Especially 50 years on ... gotta be a lot to talk about .... for normal people anyway.

Yeah ... wait, what ... that's just me ... the "Silent Cal" of the Class of '69 ... anyone now even know who Coolidge was?

We grew up together. We knew each other when we were young and stupid, and those stories usually never went further than us. We learned songs together, argued about the lyrics on what they meant and sometimes what they actually were. We cheered each other when asking a girl to dance. Well maybe this is the colloquial "we" because this was like never, for me. We committed the misdemeanors of youth together.

Seeing one another reminds us that it really did happen. That we lived it all. That we survived it all. Both are miracles.

But I don't have to talk to anyone to remember anything. Or everything. Why do I have to remember *everything*?

"Nick Taylor."

I politely turn and smile, immediately recognizing the voice. Although it literally has been decades. "Mary Langford."

Mary had been editor of the school newspaper. I was her sports editor. We were good buddies. I always liked talking with her.

Mary hugs me. I hate hugging.

Like a lot of people, Mary had a decent sense of humor but could never be accused of being funny. I made her laugh. I could make anyone laugh. When I felt like talking. Usually, I only cared to make myself laugh. That was enough for me.

Talking could be risky. Would people laugh with you? Or at you? Too often it was at you. Then no one was laughing at them.

Mary Langford ....

There is the eternal question of whether men and women can be just friends or will sex eventually get in the way. I come down on the side of yes. I had lots of buddies that were girls. The only way I was really popular with girls. Go figure.

One of them once told me I was a woman's man. I had never heard that before. "You listen," she said. "Most guys don't." I wasn't sure if I really listened well, or if I just didn't know what to say. I was always amazed and petrified that any girl was talking to me.

Mary and I talk first about retirement. I became a journalist and she didn't, so she is curious about my career—more about the first one in newspapers than the subsequent one in public relations.

I always wanted to be a foreign correspondent. I minored in Spanish at Kent State, journalism news as the major, because my dream was to replace Henry Kamm as *The New York Times* bureau chief in Madrid.

You could look it up, as Casey Stengel would say.

And I did work at major dailies in the US. Top 20 papers, some of them. But I haven't worked in a newsroom since the 1980s. Yet I have been in newsrooms in major markets around the world building relationships with reporters and editors.

Despite the fact journalists generally do not like PR people, many journalists remain friends. One even invited me to his book launch party in London, and the smaller, private dinner later.

Public relations let me visit almost 40 countries which, as it turns out, were quite important to clients. Foreign correspondent, no. Foreign flack, yes.

Hey, works for me.

I know enough to walk Mary through what newsrooms are like from New York to London to Moscow to Beijing and more. There is a wistful look in her eyes about the career she did not choose. But she became a teacher and I know from all accounts she was considered one of the best in her district.

There are of course many other classmates here—this is a big anniversary—so she and I agree to move on to greet them. She does, anyway. I renew my acquaintance with my beer.

There will never be a line of people waiting to talk with me. Why *would* there be, for someone who never wants to talk?

Yet I hear my name called again, and again I know the voice.

"Patty Christopher," I say.

She hugs me. I have about reached my quota for the night.

Patty was a cheerleader in school, a nurse in her career. I first got to know Patty when she and a friend of mine, Ronnie Reich, began dating in the early fall of 1967.

Ronnie suffered a compound fracture on his left hand in football practice. Patty visited him in the hospital. He asked her out. Ronnie didn't have his license yet. So he asked me to drive. Sure.

When I picked him up, he said, "Who'd you ask to go with you?" I said, "What? You just asked me to drive." He was flabbergasted.

He didn't have a lot of options at that point. So it was just Patty, Ronnie and me at the drive-in, watching *In Like Flint*. Cool Hand Nick, I was not.

I never knew what was appropriate and what was not.

Ronnie and Patty sat in the back seat. He thought I was an idiot. She thought I was an innocent. I tended to agree with him.

But she liked that in a boy. I guess it meant I was safe. So she and I stayed buddies, even after Patty and Ronnie broke up.

Patty and I talk and laugh but there are other people to see. She looks at me before moving elsewhere. "Thanks," she says. I am not sure why. I did go to calling hours when her dad died. Her parents and mine were friends at the American Legion. They went to calling hours for my dad, too.

But that's not it.

"You were a good friend in high school," she said. "You remember when yearbooks came out, you asked me to sign yours?"

Patty was the first person I saw after getting my copy our junior year, so she was the first person I asked to sign it. She said I was one of the "toughest" boys in school. Tough meant cool.

Kids still say that? I doubt it ... so what do they say now?

"Sure, why?"

"Because you kept me from crying when I saw that terrible picture of the cheerleaders hanging from the goalposts."

I remember. Patty was really skinny. I mean, *really* skinny. That pose more or less shortened cheerleader skirts and made it clear just how skinny. She was afraid people would laugh at her.

"First of all," I had said, "what other people think about you is irrelevant. Second, you're sixteen. Look at the other girls hanging from those goalposts. All of you, all of us, will grow more."

Patty smiles.

"You helped me more than you could ever know."

I am the cheerleader whisperer. Who knew?

It was a tiny moment among a million moments in high school. But tiny does not mean small. It was momentous for my friend.

Is that why we go to reunions? Moments like that one? With the people you knew when you were young? Is that why?

Patty hugs me, again. Smiles again too, and we separate.

Alone again, I look around the room. I recognize every classmate, and I remember everything about each one of them.

Every. Single. Thing.

Nicknames. Crushes. Steadies. Secrets.

Whether they could be trusted. Or trusted to turn on you.

Every. Single. Thing.

Some people say they can't remember shit, then laugh and call it the "CRS Syndrome." Usually they're joking.

But not me. I can't forget shit.

I mean I really can't forget *anything*. I remember everything.

It took me a long time to realize that this is unusual. For years, I'd meet people I hadn't seen in a long time, even years, and pick up the exact conversation from the last time. Or I'd meet people that I knew and ask them about their kids or grandkids, and remember the names and ages of all of them. I'd even go to my wife's class reunions—she went to a different, rival school—and recall stories about her classmates, too.

My wife makes me attend her class reunions. I like her friends. But she won't go to my reunions. She knows that if she does, I'll only talk with her. It's her way of making me be sociable.

Why go if you're not going to talk with anyone? She doesn't understand. No extrovert understands.

The response was almost always the same. It was not good. It wasn't that people said much of anything. It was the amazed or bemused look on their faces. You could see them wondering: What was I talking about? How did I know about that?

I would wonder, how can you not remember? Or perhaps I am that easy to forget? Or is what I have to say that uninteresting?

It was always on me. Didn't do much for my confidence. At least, until I realized this difference about me ... for example ...

Across the room, I see Dan Morgan and his wife, Rita. She was in the class ahead of ours. They owned a machine shop that served the rubber companies but sold it when they decided to retire.

Last time I saw Dan, at the last reunion I attended a decade ago, he needed a cane after injuring his knee in a fall off of a porch. As I recall, he simply tripped walking out of the house one morning.

We were not close in school, but I remember things about Dan that either he won't recall or won't want anyone else to know. Take Thursday, November 9, 1967. Junior year. There was a bonfire rally at the high school that evening, before the championship football game the next night. I had started to avoid such events. I didn't need to be part of any crowd any more.

Not once I discovered the truth. They all lied. Everybody lies.

Anyway, I had only just started dating a girl—*that* girl, the one I thought about throughout the Sixties, the one I dated for much of the late Sixties—and she asked me to meet her at the rally as she already had made plans to attend with her friends.

So I am standing in the crowd, waiting for her to break free of her friends, when the team captain incites the crowd to start a snake dance around the school and, as it turned out, far beyond.

Dan Morgan is standing next to me, his arm slung around the shoulder of Carla Morabito. He sits behind her in homeroom. She says, "Let's join the snake dance!" He says, "You're going to f___ tonight!"

She notices me watching and emits an embarrassed smile.

Would either one remember? Maybe. Probably. I doubt you forget such ... youthful interactions, as apparently happened later. But neither would like to be reminded. Especially around spouses.

I could be a thoroughly dangerous man ....

I don't like these memories, don't want many of them, in fact. But there doesn't seem much I can do about them.

Once I tried to program my mind to forget at least some things, even just the arcana that I picked up. Did you know, for instance, that the Titanic sank at 2:20 a.m.? No? Not real useful, is it? All that happened as a result of my trying to forget is that I remember what I told myself to forget.

But to those who know about my memory, I am something else.

One day, years into my career at a major public relations firm, I am holding court in a meeting, I hear the CEO page me "Nick Taylor, please call extension 1010." Maybe a client is in trouble. That often comes to me. So I call.

"Hey," he says, "what was that line from *The Princess Bride* again?"

I cannot believe this. But I know exactly what he wants. "Hello," I say, "my name is Inigo Montoya. You killed my father. Prepare to die."

For those who can't remember shit, I can be a godsend. If he made any money on a bet, I should lay claim to a commission. Settling bets or sating curiosities aside, infinite memory has often been a godsend to me, too.

Yet it can make me lazy, as I often substitute memory for thought.

It took me a long time to realize that for me, there is no such thing as time. Time may pass, but there is no past.

Everything that has ever happened, just now happened.

Like the music and how my imagination lived in certain songs.

Like a drivers license becoming a declaration of independence.

Like the task at the funeral home of checking the body of a friend killed in the war because his father could not look at his boy.

Like the first kiss—I actually sideswiped her lips—with THAT girl, the one that every guy in school wanted, and the one that nobody could see with me.

"Summer of '69" is the song playing now, not a song in my head. *Thank you, Bryan Adams. I'm sure we'll hear it again.*

Were *those* the best days of my young life?

No, that would be summer of '68. For those who recall or have read about 1968 with wars and assassinations and protests and more, that might be hard to fathom. But summer of '68 ... well.

Would she be here?

Okay so where did that come from? Of all the thoughts I've had so far this evening, I haven't had that many about her. I've never heard that she attended any reunion. Why come now?

"Things I'd Like to Say" by New Colony Six pops into my head. Yeah, OK, maybe there are things I'd like to say to her.

Was I hoping that she and I would get married some day? Well, yeah, maybe ... was that more her than me? *But so what?* She's the one who started talking about marriage.

That girl. THAT girl....

STOP IT.

Am I doomed to remember every single lyric of every single song every single time I think about anything at all?

That would be a yes.

I drink a little more beer and look at all these classmates from so many years ago.

Good Lord, who are all these old *people? Wait ... they think the same thing about you, bub.*

But in a slow-motion, strobe-light metamorphosis, I see them first as they are, old people, and then as they were, young people. This is how I remember them. Every single thing about them, past and present layered as one.

Robin Williams joked, "If you can remember the Sixties, you weren't really there."

What a bunch of bullshit.

I remember the Sixties. Every. Single. Thing.

Where is Tom Baker?

CHapteR 2

In one ear, I hear Ray Turner giving me a tutorial on The Wrecking Crew. In the other, I am ingesting all the music that plays.

Jimi Hendrix is singing "Purple Haze." I hear the words that many people thought he said, not the words he actually said.

Kiss this guy?

Kiss the sky?

Wait, what?

My grandkids say that all the time. It is sticky. Just like "get off my lawn," for, uh, other generations.

Seemed like Jimi Hendrix was saying "kiss this guy," but really it was "kiss the sky." These days, the first version might make more sense. But not in 1967.

Ray headed the A/V Club, one of the rather limited number of school clubs at least until the late Sixties. If the word "geek" had been invented, it would have been applied to its members. Certainly "nerd," or "nurd" as it was then spelled, was in vogue for those who were not. But it was a nasty pejorative at the time.

The kinds of clubs at school you could join started to expand late in the Sixties. There was a folk club for those who agreed Bob Dylan had sold out. There was a ski club for those who wanted to try the speed bumps that passed for ski trails in Northeast Ohio, like my friend Tom Baker. It led him to a career as a ski coach.

That wasn't good enough for Barry Wilson and Jack Simms. Or rather, there wasn't anything available that appealed to them. Or maybe it was that no other club would take them. I don't know.

But Barry and Jack were brilliant and not a little bored. So they decided to create a club that could be made available to everyone regardless of race, creed, religion ... or intelligence. Fools of America (FOA). Really. Makes me smile even now.

I was, more or less, present at the creation. They came up with the idea one day at lunch when talking about the paucity of clubs of interest. I could hear them howling from across the cafeteria. I asked what was so funny, and they explained as best they could around laughing so hard. I joined the club on the spot.

It cost you a buck to join and in return you got a laminated card confirming your membership in Fools of America, which was in small print, and FOA in large print. Looked pretty legitimate. It was sort of the club for people who, like Groucho Marx, wouldn't be a member of a club that would have them as a member. Barry and Jack bagged more than 200 members who, like me, wanted to pad their resume.

I bet they were the model for Phineas and Ferb ....

Later, Barry would instigate one of the most infamous incidents in school history. The Gunpowder Plot.

At first, I didn't fathom the appeal of the A/V Club. It didn't take long for me to get it. The appeal was tiered on a lot of levels. First, you got out of many classes to go set up projectors and screens for other classes. That much was obvious. But I didn't know what they did at meetings. Were they like the Freemasons? Were there secret rituals with virgins? Maybe they watched old movies like *The Guns of Navarone.*

Heroic war movies were popular until about 1967. As sentiment turned against the Vietnam War, movies began depicting war as mean, vicious, stupid, insane, and gave us *King of Hearts, The Dirty Dozen, M*A*S*H, and Kelly's Heroes.*

Or maybe when the A/V guys could get them, films featuring, say, Brigitte Bardot. These guys were resourceful, after all.

Second, you learned the rudiments of electronics technology. And eventually that led many A/V Club members into computers. Some classmates went to Apple and other tech giants.

Grandkids are probably hackers. I smile at the thought.

That smile excites Ray, thinking I am a disciple in music production. Who am I to ignore the gospel according to George Martin? But The Wrecking Crew is not news to me. Ray gets louder as he discusses a topic of particular interest to him if only some to me.

Meanwhile, Jimi Hendrix is still beating up his guitar.

It wasn't until just a few years ago that I realized my wife thought it was "kiss this guy." We were driving somewhere and while we rarely listen to old music any more, we stumbled on the song.

"Did you just say *'s'cuse me while I kiss this guy?*"

"That's the lyric, right?"

"No. It's *'s'cuse me while I kiss the sky!*"

"Are you sure?"

"Who's the one with the memory?"

My wife doesn't like to be wrong. Neither do her siblings. My brother-in-law once said, "You can always tell a member of this family, but you can't tell them much." But my wife has a terrible memory. She knows I must be right.

"OK. I guess that makes more sense. I always thought it was 'kiss this guy.' I thought that was pretty bold for the time."

This is not the first such debate I have had about songs. How many millions of us thought the lyrics to "Louie Louie" were ....

"You know the Wrecking Crew did the intro to, 'Wouldn't It Be Nice.' " Ray is giving me a history lesson. Me, who loves history. Me, who can never forget anything. *Anything.*

But I stay tuned to this station.

I wonder if anyone ever screwed up those lyrics. Well, I had a hard time at first deciphering all of "Good Vibrations." But not "Wouldn't It Be Nice." Not when THAT girl would sing it to me.

Instead, I am attacked by thoughts of all the songs where I was not quite sure of the words. I lived on the island of misfit lyrics.

This started early, in kindergarten. First day, the teacher, Carol Weil, says, "All right everyone. We are going to sing 'America!'" This was 1956. Everyone still sang or played patriotic music.

Although I was five, I had never heard the song before. I didn't know the lyrics. My exposure to music was limited to Lawrence Welk. This was not on his playlist. *Wunnerful, wunnerful.*

Ha … you had to be there to know that one.

So I faked it, and I handled it until we got to "Of thee I sing." I just could not make out the words. For the longest time, I mumbled it as "Of V-I-C," you know, "Vee Eye See."

Nobody ever called me on it.

That was crucial. You couldn't admit you didn't know the words to a song. So you sang it and made up your own words.

Like, say, "Summer in the City." Big hit for The Lovin' Spoonful in the summer of 1966. One day that summer, I was at the Kilkenny house in our new housing allotment. Eventually they had ten kids, but only seven then. The three oldest, Steve, Greg and Debbie, were about my age. So what was one more kid hanging out?

Greg was my best friend in the neighborhood. I spent much of the Sixties at his house. It was a safe haven, a safe house. And that meant the world to me then … it still does even now.

In the summer, Mr. Kilkenny installed a screen behind the open garage door, and Greg and some of his siblings or other kids in the neighborhood, played cards, pingpong etc., in that garage.

I could not make out the line about how it was so hot that even the back of your neck was grimy and gritty. But I liked the song and we all sang along. It fit a summer without air conditioning.

I just sang it as, "back of my neck getting oh so pretty …."

17

Greg, one of my best friends, never said anything. Maybe he didn't know, either. But his sister, Debbie, knew the words.

"Did you say 'back of my neck getting oh so pretty?'" she giggled.

"No!" I said.

"Yes you did."

"No I didn't."

"Then what are the words?"

"You know them as well as I do. I'm not repeating them." I mean, your manhood is at stake here. Certainly with a girl.

Or like, say, "Friday on My Mind." Big hit in winter of 1967 for The Easybeats. The last lines of the first verse are about how s-l-o-w the week goes until he can see his girl again. Friday is always on his mind. And then moves to the chorus about soon having fun in the city. I never had any trouble with the song except that first line of the chorus. So I sang it as, "Gonna head for Nimbo City."

Never mind there was no such place in the United States. This band was from Australia, right? Had to be a Nimbo City there ... I sang it every time it was on the radio and never got called out.

Or like, say, "A Little Bit of Soul." Big hit in the summer of 1967 for The Music Explosion, actually a group from nearby Mansfield. There is a line in the third verse about how you have a party that is flat because there is nothing grooving. A cipher, to me. So I just sang it as, "And when your body has gone to see somebody groovy," I even belted it out as loud as I could, and never got called out.

But that did eventually happen.

In December 1967, Ronnie Reich and I were driving to the mall for some Christmas shopping—we weren't really friends until I got a license before him, but then were great pals—and were listening to "Daydream Believer" by the Monkees.

"*Cheer up please, Regeen,*" Ronnie crooned.

The first time we hit the chorus, I let it slide. Not the second. "Wait a minute," I stopped singing. "It's *sleepy Jean.*"

"That doesn't make any sense."

"It makes a lot more sense than *cheer up please, Regeen*. You ever know a girl named Regeen?"

"It's just short for Regina."

"It's *sleepy Jean*, Ronnie."

"Tell you what, you sing it your way, and I'll sing it my way."

"Fine."

"Fine."

I am still learning that there are songs I've sung for decades but still don't know the lyrics for sure. Just this winter in Cancun with friends who own a time share, my wife and I learned that we never knew the right words to "Looking Out My Back Door." Great song, summer of 1970. I always thought the lyric was *memory's an elephant*. But they're not. It's *tambourines and elephants*. For the record, I like my lyrics better.

That discovery led my wife to admit to me: "Well, remember 'Kind of a Drag?'"

"Yeah sure, The Buckinghams, winter 1967. Why?"

"Well, when they sang 'kind of a drag,' I thought it was Canada Dry, you know, the ginger ale. Nobody ever said anything so maybe nobody else knew the words, either."

We had a good laugh on that one ... and on all of them.

So not only do I remember all the lyrics, even the wrong ones, I remember really useless stuff. Like abortive follow-ups.

Everybody has heard Norman Greenbaum sing "Spirit in the Sky." You know, where he was gonna go when he died. But I also remember his follow-up, "Canned Ham." And that I remember this is all the more weird, because these days, who even knows what a canned ham is?

I may be the only person in the world who knows this song, other than maybe Norman Greenbaum or his mother.

Everyone has heard the Five Man Electrical Band sing "Signs." Anthem for an old generation, perhaps, but you still hear it played. You know, signs telling you what to do ... or mostly not.

But here again I remember the next not quite hit single, "You Were Absolutely Right." I always thought that it seemed an apology to a girlfriend who, of course, was right all along. Maybe one or two other people remember that one. Who knows.

But, *who* remembers stuff like this? Like I said, this is *real* useful in my life. Hey, still waiting for that call up to Jeopardy.

And, too, for every action, there is an equal and opposite reaction. Newton's third law of physics as applied to music means sometimes *you* changed the lyrics, and it was for fun.

Tony McAuliffe, who lived in our neighborhood, was maybe the most obscenely funny person I ever knew. So in 1966, when everyone was singing "Wild Thing"—and everyone in the world still knows these lyrics, about how she can make his heart sing—

Tony came up with his own lyrics, you know ... about how she makes his *thing* swing.

And that wasn't even the bawdiest one. There was this song by the Rascals ... well, we won't go there just now.

Ray is still talking about the Wrecking Crew. "And they did a lot of the work for The Monkees, too."

Appropriate. The Monkees used Jimi Hendrix as an opening act because Mickey Dolenz liked him. Jimi flipped off the crowd. I wonder if Ray knows that too.

"Ray, I don't know what you know about the music business, but I know it is not about music, it is about money."

I think everything *is about money. Jaded, much?*

I continued, "I know a fellow who was the bassist for a group that had a number one hit and some other smaller successes, too. In 1968, his group was on tour when what would be their next hit came out. The crowd wanted them to play it, but they had never heard it before. It was recorded in the studio without them.

"The crowd just thought they were being jerks. As in, go buy the record if you want to hear the song."

Ray nods. "Yes, I know. But it was still about the music to

musicians," Ray speaks in a slow, plodding voice. He almost sounds like a metronome. But he is a good guy. I would never laugh at him.

I decided long ago—in high school, among these people in fact—never to laugh at others. Not over what is beyond our control. Too many had laughed at me. I knew how that felt. I also knew that is why many classmates never showed at reunions.

Greg Kilkenny is one of them. He will never attend a reunion. He is still one of my best friends, we stay in touch although he lives in southern Virginia.

Greg was tall and gangly. He liked sports and was good at all of them. Yet there were people in his class, one ahead of me, who never let him forget he looked goofy to them. But not me.

Time doesn't heal all wounds.

Time doesn't do anything but look at you as it passes by. It's what *you* choose to do with that time.

Anyway, I am filing away a few things about the Wrecking Crew that I might use in a decade if I see Ray again.

Speaking of disciples, I talked Ray into going to church with me a few times in high school when I was trying to save the world. Ray appreciated the music production. The sermon, not so much.

In high school, I could fit in with any group. Somehow, I could move effortlessly across most groups. I never stayed for long. But I was curious about people. I thought everybody had a story to tell. They were all interesting to me. Like Ray. Yet I was not so much learning from them as through them.

Mom was an 8-to-5 executive secretary at one of the big rubber companies headquartered in Akron. Dad was a 4-to-12 foundry worker at an auto plant in Cleveland.

I was always by myself. I never minded being alone.

Dad subscribed to *Newsweek* (I can still see the cover of the first issue we received, JFK in a top hat at his inauguration back in 1961), and I devoured every issue. I even read encyclopedias.

"What I Am" ... *Edie Brickell and the New Bohemians. Yeah, I*

knew what I knew and thought what I thought.

I knew what everything *could* mean, just not what it *did* mean. Did I know that much? How important was what I knew? Did I think about the right things? How useful was what I thought?

I learned a lot from others.

But still, the most important lesson was one I learned by myself. What other people think of you is absolutely irrelevant. It's what you think about yourself that is important. And sometimes you don't know what you really think until the words come tumbling out of your mouth before your mind catches up.

I already knew this lesson before I gave it to Patty Christopher. I'd like to say I remembered this lesson all my life, but it'd be a lie.

Ray and I are still talking about music.

"Know what the first psychedelic song was?" He smiles.

"Psychotic Reaction," I say. It is an immediate and automatic response.

Yeah ... don't waste my time ....

You could also say it was the first hard rock song, the first acid rock song, the first ... unfortunately, Count Five never counted past one and done.

I am afraid I have disappointed Ray, taken away his opportunity. But Ray grins and asks me another one.

"So, Nick, what was the original title of 'Brown Eyed Girl?'"

And I laugh because I know. "'Brown Skinned Girl.'"

Ray laughs, too.

Yet it is the music that I hear talking to me. It always did.

There are those who say the Sixties were unlike any other time. I think this is true insomuch as every era or epoch is unique. But that doesn't inherently mean that an era is special. My parents never thought of the Thirties as special. Only a calamity.

What was so special about the Sixties? Were wars, famines, riots, demonstrations, assassinations, drugs, rebellions, all that new? Or were we just more aware of everything happening then?

Maybe.

Were there people who cared about stopping the Vietnam War because they thought it was wrong? Yes. Were there more people who wanted an end to the war before they were drafted?

Maybe.

Were there people who cared about stopping racism, poverty and other societal evils? Yes. Were there more people who thought of these as abstracts that had nothing to do with them?

Maybe.

Were there people who attended protests because they thought our voices could reach those in power? Yes. Were there more who went because it might be fun or they could get laid?

Maybe.

It was a generation that wanted to think that it made a difference, that it changed the world. Some of that is true. Not all of it is good. Just because that's cynical, doesn't mean that it's not true.

The Who sang "My Generation." But the only people trying to put *me* down were my generation. I wanted *them* to fade away.

Maybe if anything was truly special about that time, it was the music.

Realizing that someone is waiting for Ray, I deftly intervene.

"So, Ray, are you retired? If so, what are you doing these days?" Then I notice, surprised, that someone is waiting for me, too.

"I'm the projectionist at the Highland Theater," he says.

I look at him. "I thought that was your job in high school."

Ray laughs. Pat Paulsen laughed more than Ray Turner.

"It was," he explained. "The theater was closed for a long time. New owners came in—they knew people liked the really big screens at old theaters—and they called me to come back."

It's deja vu, all over again.

I wonder if Ray knows anything about Yogi Berra.

CHαptεR 3

Mike Hawkins is waiting to talk with me.

"No Particular Place to Go" by Chuck Berry pops into my head, and I know exactly why.

Mike is whistling Beethoven, then stops and grins at me. Behind him his wife, Sam, the former Samantha Race, also a classmate, is chatting with the greeters handing out name tags. Mike was the leader of the only clique that mattered to me. For far too long, in fact.

Once you reached junior high, you started the migration from one class to the next, but with everyone from your own homeroom. Mike was the leader of 7F. More like the king of seventh grade.

"It's Good to Be King." Thank you, Tom Petty.

Yeah, it's a wonder anything ever stays with me, given how much stuff pops into my head, but nothing ever leaves. And as Tom Petty rattles around in my head, I suppose it *is* good to be king. Like I would know what it was like in junior high.

Mike seemed a natural born leader, blending charisma, charm, boldness, decisiveness, snarkiness, tolerance and more. He was also the best dancer I ever saw. I was so envious.

But one big lesson I learned from him was how to appreciate the provenance of music. It was a lesson I never forgot. But I used it for a lot of reasons beyond any interest in just music.

The Beatles owned 1964. But Chuck Berry still had a hit: "No Particular Place to Go."

Mike—a saxophonist in the junior high band like me—and I were talking about that song one day after band practice.

"Chuck Berry is one of the major talents in music," Mike said.

"Who's Chuck Berry?" I said.

Without other siblings to observe, I really had no knowledge or context regarding most songs or artists. I just knew what I liked.

Mike stared at me. You know the look: *are you for real?* "You're joking, right? Chuck Berry is one of the most influential rock and roll performers. He didn't just sing, he told stories."

I resisted the urge to say, "Oh, you mean *that* Chuck Berry." I already looked dumb to Mike. Why look stupid, too?

"Johnny B. Goode," "Roll Over Beethoven," "Sweet Little Sixteen," "Maybelline," " Brown-Eyed Handsome Man." The list went on. I knew some of these. How could I not know who did them?

I realized later that the answer was easy. I didn't pay much attention to music in the Fifties. And I didn't have a radio or record player for a long time.

The state controlled all access to music. My parents. We attended a Baptist church. Rock and roll was disdained. And dancing was of the devil.

In fact, one joke about getting married was that the pastor would tell you that you could not have sex standing up because it looked too much like dancing. Actually, it does, kinda.

So I had to listen on the sly. And I never did learn how to dance.

If my parents played music, it was Mantovani. It was music that inspired … elevator companies. I bet it played nonstop at Otis. I might have paid more attention if Chuck Berry had written "Roll Over Mantovani." I wanted to roll over *Mantovani*.

But in junior high, it didn't take much to make me feel dumb.

Mike didn't share my ignorance with the group. Probably

because they didn't know much about Chuck Berry, either. It wouldn't have mattered. They'd have laughed anyway. I was the dung hill of the group, and all shit flowed downhill to me. But Mike was king, and unlike most of the others, generally kind.

"Nick Taylor, good to see you!" Mike smiles.

Do I play with him or not? Maybe for a minute or two. He could dance all right. But I can dance, too.

"Mike Hawkins. Last time I saw you, you were scheduled for a hip replacement. Looks like you're moving well."

Mike smiles. "Thanks for asking," he says. "I'm doing well."

He doesn't know about the infinite memories in my head. I often didn't say any more than necessary with the group. It made me a target. So none of these people knows much about the memory.

"How are Jared, Seth and Marty and all the grandkids?" He might not have gaped back when I didn't know Chuck Berry. But he is gaping now as I know his sons and daughter.

"Jared and Seth still in London? Marty still at the art museum?"

Mike looks amazed.

Come one, come all to see the Amazing Memory Man! Step right up folks, don't be shy now, and ask Memory Man when Kosygin met LBJ at Glassboro State (June 23-25, 1967), when Jane Fonda visited Hanoi (July 1972), when ...."

STOP IT.

Good grief.

But as easy as this is for me, I relent. I like him, after all.

Yeah, the devil made me do it, just like Flip Wilson. Ha.

"I remember your kids because you were so proud of them, told me all about their careers when we were talking about our kids." Mike smiles again. He doesn't think I'm a stalker after all. I think. But I always have to be careful how I unleash this memory.

Mike surprised me for years after high school. I didn't make all the reunions, but when I did, he was there and knew lot about my career.

Mike also worked on the school paper. Social Editor. Of course I remember. He thought about journalism, maybe why he vicariously followed my career, but became a teacher. He liked it, but took 30 years and out. I remember that from an earlier reunion.

I ran into him in the 1980s at a youth baseball game across town. His son was playing my son. I recognized Mike right away. I had to introduce myself. He had no idea who I was. I had a beard that rivaled Nebuchadnezzar, the James Harden of his day.

We spent most of the game catching up. He told me he was a teacher. I told him this didn't surprise me, because he cared about people and he was good with people. There was a sincerity and earnestness about him. At least as he matured.

But the truth is, I was surprised. Nobody disliked teachers more than Mike. He was hard on them, sometimes to their faces.

Mike was a smart ass. One reason we got along pretty well. I was sarcastic with others in the clique when I thought I could get away with it. Not infrequently, I had to be oblique. Mike always got my barbs and either laughed hard or tried hard not to laugh at all.

Then one day, a hard ass kicked his smart ass.

Jenny Gilliam.

Mrs. Gilliam was a social studies teacher in the high school.

She taught some other classes, too, but that is what she taught sophomores. She was a good teacher. And when she choreographed the school musical, we found out she could sing and dance. She was shapely and lovely, too.

Of more interest to boys was the fact that the last button fastened on her blouse was four from the top—all the boys counted, math infiltrating social studies—and that showed a lot of bra and boob.

One day in class, she bent over and one of those boobs popped out. You know the sound in those cartoons where a character's jaw hits the ground? That's pretty much what happened.

She gasped. She sputtered. She put her boob back in place. But it was out there for a while. Then she ran out of the room.

Everyone in the school knew within minutes. There didn't need to be social media for *this* to get around. And everyone was waiting to see how she would respond.

The next day, a group of us was loitering around the door to her classroom. She was coming down the hall.

I usually, if not always, knew when to keep my mouth shut tight. But Mike was about to learn this lesson in Mrs. Gilliam's Charm School for Boys.

"Here comes the beautiful Mrs. Gilliam," he said, a bit too loud.

Mrs. Gilliam stopped inches in front of Mike, then swiftly put one hand on his chest and shoved him into the lockers. You could do this as a teacher back then and get away with it. People still trusted leaders, and that included teachers. If you said anything to your parents, they might easily say you had it coming.

I remember the first time I dressed for a varsity football home game. I was a sophomore. Freshman were not permitted to play high school sports. You could participate in marching band because there weren't enough kids in the band. But not sports.

Everything about high school football was exciting. Running out on the field at the start of the game, running through calisthenics and various plays. People cheered. If I now pass a stadium at night and see the lights, I can still smell cigarette smoke, too, even if you can't smoke there anymore.

We scored two quick touchdowns against a smaller school, then let up and the other team scored before the half. We weren't in the locker room ten seconds at halftime when the coach—generally known as that bald-headed bastard—slammed senior receiver Scott Jones into the lockers and screamed at us.

We scored four times in the second half—twice by Jones— and never let the other team past midfield. When the game was over, I heard Jones, the target of that wrath, mutter, "Thank God."

Mrs. Gilliam had clearly thought through how to respond to the first signs of insurrection after accidentally flashing her class and so demonstrate to the school that she was in complete control.

"You have a problem, Hawkins?"

"Uh, no ma'am," he stuttered. You could have heard a bra drop.

"Good," she said, straightening herself. "See me after class."

Mike told us about the meeting later. She told him he was smart and had potential, but he was wasting it all. Get serious, she told him. You've got two more years here, then what?

If Mrs. Gilliam could make him focus on something other than what was in her blouse, maybe he could have a positive impact on people, too. He started thinking about becoming a teacher.

And as I recall, Mrs. Gilliam never buttoned up any higher.

That was late spring 1967. I had just abandoned the clique. But in junior high, the clique was everything. Mike was our leader and I never thought he was that interested in me. Most of the time Mike and I talked in junior high, it was about me not being an idiot.

I took most such exchanges with the group as heaped disdain. That's usually what I got from most of the others.

Mike, not so much.

At the end of the school year in eighth grade, spring 1965, there was a junior high dance held in the high school gym.

"Annie Dobbs is going to talk to you," Mike told me at the dance.

Wait, what?

"She's moving to another school district. But she has a crush on you and wants to say she wishes she got to know you better."

Wait, what?

"Be nice to her. She's a good kid."

Wait, what?

So yes, I was nice to Annie Dobbs. I would have been, anyway. But I would never have known she liked me if he hadn't said so.

I didn't have to look up obtuse in the dictionary. All I had to do was look in the mirror. I was flat out dense.

A girl liked *me*?

Nobody liked me.

Wait, what?

Maybe Mike was just waiting for me to show some maturity.

***

"Mike, are you still playing guitar?"

I know the answer but take this time to sift some memories.

In summer 1964, before eighth grade, Mike did what thousands of teen boys across the country were doing: he started a band.

Did the rock and roll music of the Fifties prompt a lot of kids to start their own bands? Sure. But that was nothing compared to a simple confluence of events and trends in the early and mid-Sixties.

First, The Beatles rocked the world with "Please Please Me" and never stood still until they could no longer stand one another.

Second, scores of other British, and later American groups, began to emerge, many of them disappearing within several years as The Beatles again changed the direction of rock and roll.

And third, baby boomers by the thousands became teenagers every day and began heaving money at the hot new sounds.

In Northeast Ohio alone, where we lived, dozens of local groups created what the labels marketed as the "Ohio Sound," yielding such hits as "A Little Bit of Soul" and "Yummy Yummy." Over the years, many other local stars emerged, such as Joe Walsh, Chrissie Hynde, The Black Keys and more.

If four working-class heroes from the backwater of Liverpool could make it, well, they were an inspiration for a generation, both for the music and the drugs.

"Kicks" by Paul Revere and the Raiders pops into my mind. That was one warning from the midnight ride of Paul Revere that we should have heeded in America.

A few years ago, the media fixated on the Internet of Things (IOT). It never really captured public imagination so the media moved on, as they always do. But in the Sixties, there was what I call the Democratization of Music (DOM). It was, I think, the first wave of the democratization of almost everything. I mean, anyone could form a band.

There were few such mass opportunities before that change. Now anyone can try to become a star on YouTube, Instagram, *America's Got Talent* and more. There are few lines of demarcation in society that prevent anyone from attempting almost anything.

Mike was lead singer and played guitar and sax. Andy Longstreet played lead guitar. Rich Milner, a year younger, played bass. John Mixon played drums. John and Andy also were in our class. Mike and the band played songs that were popular, songs that they liked, and frankly, at first, songs simply that they could play.

The band played at junior high dances, competing with a rival band of ninth graders whose lead singer later became a lawyer, but even then still sang weekends at local hangouts.

In the late Seventies, my wife and I saw Sonny Geraci—who had two national hits, "Time Won't Let Me" with The Outsiders in 1966 and "Precious and Few" with Climax in 1972—in a city where I was working at the newspaper. We didn't know he was there, having just stopped for a drink. Geraci must have worked during the week, and performed on weekends. Maybe he couldn't give it up.

I think it was hard for many musicians to abandon that dream, more so for those who however briefly tasted fame. In the end of course, we all have to make a living.

As we moved into high school, Mike and his band played private parties, college mixers and more. They were regularly booked. They were a good cover band but never attempted any original music, so never cut any demos, at least as far as I know. They were talented and creative, but apparently not innovative and original.

I think the difference between great cover bands and even all the one-hit wonder groups much less all the successful bands back then, was original music. We remember one-hit wonders, but not great cover bands, even if these last were markedly better.

There were not exactly a lot of oldies in the Sixties: rock and roll was relatively new, and rock was only just starting to morph into various genres. So a cover band cutting a record either would be cutting a record on a song still in play, or not far removed from the charts, or hopelessly anachronistic given style changes.

Amazing what fifty years of music will do. Now there are fantastic, and successful, cover bands. My favorite is the MonaLisa Twins.

Once, I asked Mike if he was writing any songs. He said he didn't have time. He wasn't arrogant but never lacked confidence. And he was a good writer, as I saw later on the school paper. I didn't believe his answer. Maybe he didn't have it in him. Maybe he didn't think he had it in him. Maybe he tried and failed. I hope it was the latter. At least later, he would never have wondered.

After we graduated, band members went separate ways. Mike went to the University of Akron and married Sam while still in school. Andy got a job after graduation, got married that fall and had a kid inside a year. John became a cop. Rich moved away.

I think this likely happened to most of the thousands of bands that formed in the Sixties. Maybe it still happens to most bands.

"The Low Spark of High Heeled Boys" ... *Traffic* ... Wait, what ... yeah ... youngsters ... playing with toys ....

I look at Mike as he is talking about his kids and grandkids.

I knew at the time that my interest in the provenance of rock and roll, whether it was the Ohio Sound or other, was less spurred by that one short exchange about Chuck Berry than by a growing desire to know what I thought everyone else knew.

And then to know more than them about anything and everything.

I started to use knowledge and memory to survive psychological hand-to-hand combat. Then I just used it to keep a safe distance.

What is school for, if not to learn?

As God is my witness, I will never look stupid again. My apologies, Margaret Mitchell ... hey, that was pretty funny.

STOP IT.

"I'm in a duo," Mike is saying. I think of how many others

returned to music after retirement. "We play at wineries and brewpubs in the area. I'll send you our schedule. Come out sometime. It's music you'll remember."

Pretty sure he's right.

CHapteR 4

Rwell Crowe walks in the room.
There has been a continuous crescendo as classmates talk, but it falters to a diminuendo and then all the way to rock-bottom quiet.

Who is this guy? He sure as hell *looks* like Russell Crowe.

This is not, of course, Russell Crowe. But he is famous in his own circles. And there is a reason he is not immediately recognized. I know who he is. I have seen his photo on his album covers. Long, brown hair. Hands on his saxophone. Slip of a smile.

"Was it something I said," he says, and everybody laughs.

Most people still don't know who he is, except a few of us, so they go back to their conversations, still curious about his identity.

Faux Crowe seeks out a drink and then a friend, Wes Conners. I know from Facebook they've stayed in touch. Wes and his family even stayed with Faux Crowe on the West Coast. Before long, Faux Crowe wanders by and looks at my name tag.

"Scott Carson, I presume?"

"Hahahahahahhahahahahahahahahahahahahahahaha!"

We all have different laughs. What I mean is that we each have a raft of individual laughs that can be triggered. Belly laughs. Derisive snorts. Short sniffs. Long riffs. Nobody has just one type of laugh.

When I am surprised by something funny, I laugh in staccato.

Dave Stringer is grinning at me.

"Boots Randolph, I presume?" Dave returns the favor and laughs hard. We shake hands.

Dave is a successful jazz saxophonist in LA. He's done some albums himself, but he's a session guy still in demand. Dave transferred senior year from another high school. I sat next to him in band and next to him in government. He had an impish smile and infectious laugh, and he used both a lot.

He didn't know anyone, of course, so I tried to be friendly at least until he made friends. Turns out that I was one of them. We spent a lot of time together and talked about a lot of things. He turned me on to Miles Davis, John Coltrane and other jazz players.

Dave was already ticketed to the University of North Texas, which had a music program that could help him launch his career. He had a lot of friends already in collegiate music programs and regaled me with their stories. They were more ribald than I would have guessed, but then what did I know of college? It scared me.

The story that I remember most involved a band director who was brilliant, and also a bastard. He liked to belittle his students. "You're not a man until you get laid," he would scoff at the men. One time when the marching band was on the road, a late-night visit to the band director changed his tune. Dave's friend banged on the director's door, screaming: "I'm a man, I'm a man!"

"So, Scott Carson, you ever become a football coach?"

Scott Carson was an all-state football player at the school from which Dave had transferred from and who later played in the Big 10. When Dave found out I was on the football team, he christened me as Scott Carson. I wish.

"The closest I came to sports was a few feature stories I wrote for newspapers on athletes," I said. "Raymond Berry, Dorothy Hamill. Sorry to disappoint you, Boots."

Yeah, Boots! I just had to return the favor.

35

What I didn't tell him was that I had handled crisis management for a few high-profile athletes and other celebrities when they got themselves into very public trouble. Dave would know all this, just as I knew about his music career, if I had bothered to stay in touch. Maybe he heard about all of it on the news, just not about me behind the scenes.

On the one hand, the summer after graduation was dedicated to THAT girl and little else, except freaking out about college.

"Too Busy Thinking About My Baby" by Marvin Gaye starts spinning in my head. Yeah, that was about it for the summer of '69 ... my girl ....

In fact, my parents planned a six-week student tour of Europe as a graduation present early that summer, but I declined. I couldn't be away from THAT girl, that long.

Even my wife thinks that was crazy. I guess ....

Besides, I spent that summer looking backward. It had taken me until junior year to figure out high school. And then it was over. I was terrified about college, the new great unknown.

On the other hand, I never stay in touch with anyone. Tom Baker and Greg Kilkenny are the only occasional exceptions.

Even good friends, I abandoned.

Like Kent Warren, who is one of the funniest people I know and who was so talented he wrote jokes for greeting cards. We met when we worked at an advertising firm. He was a copywriter, and I was the writer for the fledgling public relations unit.

Or like Allen Rosen, who was the longtime features editor for one of the best big regional papers in the nation. We met early in our journalism careers at a shitty newspaper, and both dreamed (or was it fantasized?) about working at *The New York Times*.

Two really good friends when I saw them every day at work. Once they or I moved, I lost touch. Out of sight, out of mind.

"Don't Know Why" by Norah Jones pops into my head. I really don't know why.

Still talking with Dave, I laugh to myself. Because the random thought that pops into my mind is completely appropriate to the conversation. Norah Jones went to North Texas, too.

Dave and I talked about a lot of things all that senior year. These were my most serious conversations, other than with THAT girl. Dave was not the only person with whom I talked about Vietnam, but he was one of the few with whom I discussed the war on an intellectual basis.

With most people, at least from what I saw on television, emotions were raw and it was impossible to separate intellect and emotion. The latter always won.

Ho, Ho, Ho Chi Minh!

Hell no, we won't go!

Hey, hey LBJ, how many kids did you kill today?

Dave was curious and thoughtful, not judgmental. That does not mean he failed to reach conclusions or hold convictions. He did. But we could have debates and arguments, in the true sense of these words, and never draw blood. These started with Vietnam.

Would there be a draft lottery? If so, when? And what would happen to us if we drew a low number? Would college deferments continue? If so, how long? Would the war end before we got out of college? Would Nixon bring troops home as per his campaign pledge? Why was the US, arguably the greatest military power in the world, losing this war? Why was the US even there? ... the disputed domino theory?

The last time Dave and I met was at Thanksgiving break in 1969. He was home from college and we ran into each other at the mall. The My Lai massacre had just been reported.

Dave and I went to a nearby Red Barn, a local hamburger chain that was cheaper than McDonald's, and over syrupy Cokes talked about the first few months of college, and of course the war.

Was My Lai the real indication of what this country was about? Neither of us thought so. We promised to stay in touch.

It would be hard for people today to understand those times. The war was always a backdrop but was rarely discussed, at least in high school. College was an entirely different matter, maybe because you were a lot closer to getting thrown into the fire.

But not high school. My biggest discussion about the war other than with Dave was April 27, 1968, the night of the heavyweight title bout after Muhammad Ali had been stripped of the title over his opposition to the war and refusal to serve in the armed forces. Was Ali right to refuse? Was it right to take away his title? But even that discussion—over poker with Tom and Tim Baker and a few others—was not really on Vietnam.

Dave and I did not discuss battles. We discussed who we might *know* in these battles. Already people who had graduated from our school had died in Vietnam. Not, as yet, any of our friends.

That would change, too.

Dave and I do not talk about old times, old songs, old friends or anything else as ancient as us. We pick up where we left off so many years ago, talking about what is happening in the world. Climate change, for example, the new constant backdrop.

Everybody talks about the weather, but nobody does anything about it … quoting Dorothy Parker now, bub?

"Are there more albums coming, Dave?"

"I don't know. Maybe, maybe not. I'm busy with session work. People still call me, so that's good. I can keep my own pace."

Dave has done well for himself without me as a friend. He has many friends no doubt, and legions of fans. I have done well for myself without many close friends other than my wife, who has a thousand friends.

Am I justifying a failure not to stay in touch? No. I feel no remorse or regret, not for failing to stay in touch with this friend or any other friend in my lifetime.

Still, Norah Jones nailed it. Why, I wonder, do I never call?

CHapteR 5

"The Mighty Quinn"

Tom Baker arrives.

About damn time. "The Mighty Quinn" by Manfred Mann, or should I maybe say, Bob Dylan, pops into my head. Yeah, because there is nothing in the world quite like Tom Baker ... you'll not see nothing like The Mighty Baker ... ha.

When Tom and I get together, once a year or so if he comes home, the first thing I usually say after hello is ... goodbye.

"Hello Goodbye" ... The Beatles. Yeah, I like that song. It'll be hard to get it out of my head.

Tom loves talking to people. Actually, Tom just likes to talk. I think he talks out loud to himself in the rare times he is alone. After all this time, I still enjoy talking with him, too.

"Reverend Taylor!"

This nickname, I do not mind. Even if I am no longer trying to save the world. I just help a few others do that now. Tom gives me the guy hug. And then we just start laughing. We already know what we are going to talk about tonight.

Old stories. Some will be lies. Some will be exaggerations. It's what men do. A few, well, a few stories might actually be true.

Where I could be a dangerous man, Tom, to me at least, really is.

He has no filters. I have yet to let him spend much time with my two sons, even as adults. All the things I never wanted my parents to know, I don't want my boys knowing, either.

If my family ever *did* hear these stories, I would just tell them, hey, fake news.

Like the time Tom and his twin brother Tim got their hands on a sex flick, a grainy 8mm film called *The Teacher*. I'd never seen a naked woman before. It was quite an education. Somehow, their dad knew. When he and Mrs. Baker came home, he came downstairs to the rec room, looked at our innocent faces, and said, "How was the movie?"

Mr. Baker knew everything. Well, maybe almost everything.

Like the time Tom was driving his VW Bug with Bob Stern and me, and Bob thought it would be a good idea to "pull a gaucho." For the unenlightened, this is now popularly known as mooning. Maybe the window was too small. Maybe his butt was too big. Bob, to be honest, was a big guy, he was a guard on the football team.

But Bob got his ass stuck hard in the passenger window. Mile after mile on the Akron highway and we couldn't pull him back in the car. Of course, we were laughing kind of hard at the time, too. Bob later became an elected official in another state.

As far as we know, Mr. Baker had never heard about that one.

Usually, Tom is early. Maybe his flight was late.

He lives in Park City, or so he says. I've been through the Salt Lake a number of times on business for clients, and he was never there. Training kids at Mount Hood, he usually says.

Tom is a ski coach. Not just any ski coach. His kids include a number of Olympics medalists.

I remember he had one kid who was projected to win the gold. Tom asked me to put the kid through media training to get him ready for the sports paparazzi. Sure.

One of the questions I anticipated the media would ask centered on the kid not winning the gold. "So, how do you feel about not winning the gold when everyone expected you to take it home?" The kid just blinked at me. But he realized the media would make a story out of nothing if the favorite lost.

The kid won the silver, and a teammate won the gold. When the media interviewed him after the event, the kid nailed the question that I posed during training, with the answer he worked out. "I'm so happy for my teammate winning the gold! I'm so happy to bring home the silver for my country, too! It's a good day."

Media know what they want to ask. You should know what you want to say, too. And, that was the way the kid really felt. Media can be predictable, going for the story, not the news. These are not always the same.

I am getting lost in my own head again.

When a major client, a Fortune 50 company, announced the acquisition of a competitor, the media, starting with networks, wanted to talk with the CEO. Along with a commissar from corporate communications, I was inside the in-house studio at headquarters with the CEO as he readied final thoughts for the first interview with CNBC.

The camera came on and the anchor said the next guest would be the CEO, then flashed to him so viewers would stay tuned for the interview about this blockbuster deal. The anchor would be back right after this break.

I knew what the first question would be: the news had just been announced, so CNBC and then everyone else would want to create their own story, their own angle. But the PR person assigned to help didn't offer any counsel. Maybe she was intimidated.

"Ken," I said to the CEO, "the news is already out there. CNBC needs a different angle, so the first question is going to be, why do this deal now?" He nodded. They said ten seconds ... he was back on ... and the first question was, why do this deal now?

After CNBC came CNN. The CEO looked at me and said, "So what is the first question?" I told him, and he nailed it.

I am the CEO whisperer. Who knew?

Tom and his twin, Tim, were my best buds later in high school, even when I was dating THAT girl, then in college, even when I was dating the girl who would become my wife, and beyond.

At the start of high school, I didn't know either of them except that, like me, they were on the football team. I knew they were funny. I didn't yet know they were also so much fun.

Tom ended up at my house with a few other guys in a sleepover while my parents were in Florida and my grandmother was staying at the house, in what became a legendary party. That was springtime 1967, toward the end of sophomore year. Except, there was never a party. Just a bunch of mostly stupid sophomores, a few juniors, a couple of cases of 3.2% beer, and a lot of stories. Few were true. Alternative facts, so to speak.

Tom liked the way I handled these idiots—it was a first for me to take control of the clique—and invited me to his house. We stayed friends for life. He was even in my wedding.

The twins never judged me. That doesn't mean we didn't laugh at one another, or give each other shit. We did, a lot.

Like the time their father was so pissed at them fighting all the time that he bought them boxing gloves and told them to settle it once and for all. That startled them. They put the gloves aside and talked it all out. And then the three of us laughed about it. The peace lasted a week. Once again, I was the demilitarized zone between the Baker boys.

I scan the room slowly, surreptitiously, not lingering long on any of the faces of classmates or spouses. Classmates might think I want to talk to them; spouses might think I am just weird. Only one of these is true.

Once I used that ploy Mr. Baker attempted with the boys, which while it didn't stop his boys from continually fighting, it at least slowed the frequency with two people who reported to me. They just couldn't get along in the office. I talked to each of them, then both of them, and nothing worked.

Finally, I pulled them into an empty conference room. I sat at the head of the table, each of them facing the other. "I don't know what the problem is between you two," I said. "And I really don't care if you dislike each other. But you have to find a way to work together, because neither of you is doing your job.

"And worse, your attitude toward each other is beginning to cause tension in the rest of the group because they don't want to work on a team with both of you on it. This ends now.

"So here's the deal," I stood up. "The two of you are going to sit here and talk it through until you solve the problem." I left the room. They just looked at each other for a few seconds. Then they started talking and came to an agreement not to cause each other any more problems, or hurt the others any further.

Thank you, Mr. Baker, for all the lessons. I learned a lot too about strategy from Mr. Kilkenny, when we played cards. He knew every card that had been played, which formed his strategy. He almost always won. Later, I would know every card played in business, too.

Tom, Tim, and I were friends mostly because we accepted one another as we were. Same with Greg Kilkenny. He would have been in my wedding, too, but the Navy had other plans for him, installing him in Okinawa.

It wasn't just that we didn't judge one another. We never turned on one another, either. You want to keep friends like that. They're hard to find.

You can talk all you want about such people being comfortable in their own skin, or making no demands on others. What it really means is they're not selfish.

Tim contracted familial ALS in his late twenties. After I moved back to the area, I tried to visit him as often as possible, which probably was not enough. When he died, his mom asked me to be a pallbearer. It was an honor.

Tom eyeballs my red Zin.

"A little high end, aren't you Taylor, drinking wine? We need to get a couple of beers to get this party started."

"I'm just trying to make you look a little more sophisticated in the eyes of your classmates, Tom. Even if they all know better."

Tom wanders toward the bar to fetch two beers. It might take him half the night because he will stop to talk to everyone. And minutes later—he isn't making much progress bringing our beers back and I know they'll be warm, or at least mine will when he does—Tom is laughing hard with another classmate.

Vintage Tom. I already knew I'd have to savor the wine.

CHAPTER 6

"*It hurts ....*"

Man oh man oh man oh man oh man oh man oh *man*, I did not expect to hear *this* song tonight.

Gene Pitney is singing, but this time, not just in my head.

Really?

"Boy, that is really an old song," says Petey Lucas.

Man oh man oh man oh man oh man oh man oh *man*. It hurts to be in love. At least, it did for me.

"Yeah," I make myself say about how far back this one goes, some 55 years, far past our graduation year.

So ... this song? "It Hurts to be in Love."

But really, *no shit* is what I am thinking. Gene Pitney? Who broke *his* heart to make him write that song, and then broke *mine*?

When I saw Petey drinking by himself after he arrived and went straight to the bar, I approached him. He had done me favors, so I am not about to let him drink alone tonight.

"Gene Pitney," Petey says. "I learned all his songs because of my older sisters. They played his records all the time. But then every boy in America knew *The Man Who Shot Liberty Valance*. I know I did."

"Yeah," I smiled. "So did I."

Who put together *this* playlist for the reunion? Well, thanks.

"It Hurts to Be in Love." Gene Pitney. This song used to pop in my head all the time, but not for a long, long time. Yet when I do hear it, it dies slowly in my head.

"So, Petey, are you still with the FBI in Washington, are you still having so much fun you just keep working?"

Petey was third-generation law enforcement—his dad was a state patrol officer—which always surprised me given the role that Petey played in what the media called The Gunpowder Plot. I never thought he could get a job in law enforcement, but then neither Petey, Tom or the other chemistry-class idiots were arrested much less indicted. After all, nothing *really* happened.

I liked Petey Lucas. His older sisters dubbed him "Round" as he was chubby as a kid and it stuck when some of his classmates overheard them calling him by that nickname.

I never liked nicknames, not really, and especially because of the one made up for me. I once asked Petey the genesis of the nickname and he explained. I never called him by that name.

Petey was a good guy and a nice guy. There is a difference. But you can still be both. Just as there is a difference between being an asshole and an ass, although there, too, you can be both.

Petey and I sat together in geometry, which as sophomores you were obliged to take, and we helped each other with homework. He was better at math than me, actually he was pretty good, and I benefited more than he did from this relationship.

But we became friends. And while he was considered something of a nerd, I introduced him to some of the inner circle in school, I mean the nicer ones, not those in the lower levels of hell.

Petey was the only classmate to visit me at home after I suffered a concussion in our last football game as seniors. I had spent the weekend in the hospital, going home Monday morning.

That evening, I was supposed to be on a regularly televised academic challenge with several brainier classmates: I made the cut only because the questions asked of me were on topics I knew.

My teammates, who I thought were smarter than me, included:

Chris Connor, who became a professor of Russian literature, specializing in Tolstoy, in a "Little Ivy League" school;

Phil Krakow, who became head of one of the largest non-profit charities in the state;

And Henry Richards, who owned an accounting firm, and was one of the funniest people I knew. He died a few years ago.

But I had called our coach, who taught our advanced placement classes, to suggest inserting the alternate in my place. I was glum as that afternoon wore on with nothing much to do.

Petey heard I had taken myself off the team to appear on TV and stopped by our house after school, even being thoughtful enough to bring a sports magazine for me. It was an unexpected kindness. I realized few of us really reach out to help others. Sometimes, I make myself do so. Because I know "thoughts and prayers" means nothing without action.

"I retired, but I was out of the field for some time," he says. "There are rules about retirement. I really didn't want to retire, because I loved what I did, even with all the politics that we dealt with."

I listen as Petey replies, but I am still tuned to Gene Pitney.

Growing up, I listened to all the songs on the radio, when I could. That started with Fats Domino and Elvis Presley, then Bobby Vee, Bobby Lewis and Del Shannon, then The Beatles, The Supremes and Herman's Hermits then on and on with the latest hit records.

But Gene Pitney with "It Hurts to be in Love," that was different.

This was the first rock and roll song that really meant something to me, because it was my bespoke situation. The words literally stunned me. That was *me* he was singing about.

I met THAT girl in 1962 when I started hanging with her brother. He was in our class but he had failed once in grade school. Her family lived on the other side of the new allotment where we moved, homes and streets carved into what had been farm land.

"High Above Me" by Tal Bachman pops into my head.

THAT girl really was high above me. Not that she ever thought so. No, she didn't think of me at all. I was just some idiot like her brother, as far she could see.

But starting with that first time I saw her in 1962—we both turned twelve late in the year—I was not just smitten, but something that at the time I couldn't identify or explain.

And whatever it was I felt, it was unrequited, for a long time.

High above me ....

That was Tal Bachman singing in 1999, a song that I enjoyed and sang if I heard it, and nothing more.

But Gene Pitney perfectly summed up my life in 1964. I didn't just listen to the song, or sing when it played. It hurt me to be in love. I *lived* that song. I lived *in* that song, It was *me* in that song.

That was the first time I felt that way, but not the last. From 1964 to 1968, I found myself literally living in songs that didn't just reflect or explain what was happening in my life. They *were* my life. I felt it, knew it, believed it. And it helped me cope with what was happening in my life. That is, how I felt about a girl who felt nothing for me, until one day I learned she did. How could I not know? I never knew.

I didn't appreciate how much certain songs that seemed written about romantic travails helped me until much later. Once, in the first summer when my eventual wife and I were dating, she said, "Wouldn't it be great if there was a soundtrack to life?"

We were in the car, windows down as there was no air, listening to the radio, singing with Michael Parks on "Lonesome Highway." She was surprised that I also watched Parks ride his motorcycle around the country in *Then Came Bronson*.

She was more surprised that I knew the lyrics to the expanded theme song playing on AM, the music companies eager to churn a hit from a short-lived television show.

"Lonesome Highway" . . . Michael Parks.

Yeah we laughed, then forgot about it. But she was prescient. Because songs really *are* mile markers in our lives.

Or maybe it's just me. Maybe everybody else sings along to their favorite songs as nothing more than entertainment. But I doubt it.

I know that during the Vietnam War, for example, soldiers listened to songs that talked about home, or going home, to help them get through their tour of duty. Friends told me about it. I don't think this is unusual. I think people regularly bend songs to their lives, frequently even to exact circumstances in their lives.

I think this started to become more pronounced in the 1960s, simply because of the explosion first of songs, then of genres.

Somehow I don't see people saying, boy, that Gregorian chant sure got me through the Black Plague, or gee, Beethoven's Fifth helped me out during the Battle of Waterloo.

But that's not what I'm talking about here. When I heard songs like:

"It Hurts to be in Love"

"When You Walk in the Room"

"To Love Somebody"

"Can't Take My Eyes Off You"

"Pretty Ballerina"

"Happy Together"

… and others, I thought about me and THAT girl, and wondered if she would ever like me or if I was doomed to a life without love.

It wasn't just songs that reflected what I felt for THAT girl— surely more than a crush, but what, exactly?—but a few other songs that in one way or another resonated with where I was in my life.

"Live" was a hit by The Merry-Go-Round and it was a major influence in my life at the start the summer of 1967.

Yeah … live … live until you die … live … until … you die.

This was not just a song, but a personal anthem. I've heard it said you shouldn't confuse mass music with personal philosophy. All I know is that this song at that time meant the world to me. And I learned to live and appreciate every day. I learned later that The Bangles played this song and introduced it as "our philosophy."

I never talked about this with anyone. Even with THAT girl, once we finally started dating in 1967, and I learned to my astonishment and delight that she and I could discuss just about anything.

First, I didn't have a girlfriend at the time to whom I could confide my thoughts. Even if I had one, could I talk about such thoughts with her? I didn't know what steadies discussed. And I stopped inserting myself into love songs when I started dating THAT girl.

Second, I could never dare say anything to guys in our clique. I knew how they would respond, even if any of them agreed. At best, teenage boys are carnivores and at worst, cannibals.

Third, sure, I trusted Tom and Tim Baker, and Greg Kilkenny. But I mean, how weird would all of this sound to people I counted as my friends? I never knew what was weird until it was too late.

I remember exactly the first time I heard "It Hurts to be in Love." It was a Sunday, my parents and I were headed home from church. I cadged my dad into turning the radio to rock and roll music.

Just as we were exiting the highway, I heard Gene Pitney. And it was exactly my life. I loved THAT girl, well, liked her anyway, and there was no way I could tell her. I mean, I wouldn't know what to say, even if I could get the nerve or the chance to say it.

When that song played, I commiserated on my station in life by singing lyrics I knew by broken heart.

And the first time I heard "When You Walk into the Room" by The Searchers, I was again stunned because when THAT girl walked into the room, I heard thunder booms, my telltale pounding heart.

I am parallel processing—talking with Petey, who deserves my attention—and thinking of the past, which commands it instead.

Even as my mind is sublet to other matters, I know how to sustain a conversation by asking questions. But as an FBI field agent, Petey knows how to ask questions too.

Most people just talk about themselves until they realize, if they do, that they are just talking about themselves.

Not Petey.

"Did you retire, too? Or are you still with *The Times*?"

There is a legend among classmates that I worked at one of the best dailies in the nation. I did not. I turned down a tryout offer, for a job in PR. Shocked the hell out of everyone I knew in media.

"I am retired." I tell Petey. "You know when people who are retired tell you that they're so busy and they don't know how they ever got anything when they were working? Well, it's true."

But I respect Petey too much to fall back on this rote script.

"I had the chance to travel a lot in public relations," I tell Petey. "My wife went with me. We visited a lot of places. But there is still so much more to see, so we are working through a bucket list.

"We've visited Israel, Napa Valley, New England, for example. In Napa, we hired a driver so we could do tastings at a number of wineries. In New England, we ate our weight in lobster."

All this is true, and more than I usually tell people unless they ask.

"I'm curious, Petey. How much can you tell me about some of the bigger cases you've been involved with? I have to tell you that I've been involved in some of the biggest crisis stories over the years. I know what I can and cannot share, and I know you do too. But you show me yours," I say but we both start to laugh, and then say at the same time, "and I'll show you mine."

"Deal," he says. He pauses.

"I was on Waco," he says, and immediately I know what he means.

His eyebrows arch as he recalls—I can tell that he can still see it in his mind—the siege of David Koresh and his Branch Davidian compound.

"What a cluster you-know-what that was."

A few more oldies have come and gone since Petey and I started chatting. I recall each. "Hair" ... Cowsills .... But now it is another love song in which I imagined myself: "Happy Together," by The Turtles, even as I listen to Petey.

I *did* imagine us together ... I *did* think about her all the time ... I *did* think what it would be like to hold he.

I dreamed of holding her tight, and never letting go. I dreamed again and again and again ... I imagined ... again and again and again, THAT girl and me ... being happy, together ... happy ... *together.*

Oh yeah ....

No matter how much I used "Happy Together" and other songs to express what I felt for THAT girl, I imagined that some day, a girl would say she belonged to me, and ease my mind, too.

"I had fun as a reporter," I tell Petey when it is my turn. "I covered a lot of politics, such as governors and senators. I covered a lot of other leaders and celebrities, such as, say, the chairman of the joint chiefs of staff, Olympic medal winners, and more.

"There are a lot of inherent problems attached to being in the news media. The hours suck. The pay sucks. It's hard to raise a family on the salary involved. It's hard to be there for your kids.

"So I moved into public relations. It was considerably more fun and fascinating. Because I specialized in media relations— dealing with media around the world—I usually got pulled into crisis situations when these came our way.

"There is no such thing as a crisis that does not involve media. You were on Waco. Look at media coverage of Waco and the FBI. I got people out of the media, or kept them out of the media.

"That included such crises as plane crashes, plant fires, labor issues, mergers and acquisitions, CEO ousters, corporate bankruptcies, sexual harassment allegations, racial issues including black employees finding nooses at their work stations, product recalls, government investigations—you name it, I handled it. And both in the US and in countries elsewhere around the world. It could be hard to explain to a lot of people what exactly I did."

Petey smiles. "Copy that."

"I got to where I would tell people when they asked about what I did for a living, that I saved lives. People would say, 'Oh, you must be a doctor.' 'No,' I would say. 'I'm in PR.'"

"Most people didn't know what to say next, so that usually ended the questions. It was a lot more fun to watch their faces because you knew they were baffled, and a lot less frustrating not to have to go through yet another explanation of what PR is, and is not."

I pause for several seconds.

"In the end, it's simple. It's not hard. It's just difficult. What I really did was solve problems."

Petey laughs. "Yeah, me too. You'd think it'd be easy to explain to people what the FBI does. What I did. But it's not. There's been so much put out there about the Feeb that is wrong, but accepted as truth.

"Usually people say, 'Oh, you must have caught a lot of bad people.' Well sure, that's part of it. But I spent more time in research, following leads and trails, than anything else.

"I stopped trying to explain, though. Too much energy wasted. So I used the old line, 'I could tell you what I do, but then I'd have to kill you.' People look at me to see if I'm kidding. I think because that might actually be true, they don't know what to say next. And then I laugh, they laugh, and that's the end of the questions."

"Point taken," I joke. "I won't ask too many more questions."

But, I wonder if there might have been times when we were involved in the same matter, and the first one that comes to mind is Charlie Keating and the S&L crisis in the early '90s.

His eyes grow wide.

"I was involved in the investigation," he says. "Same with some other financial fraud cases like Ivan Boesky and Michael Milken. What were you doing on the Keating case?"

"One of our clients was a law firm that had worked with Keating and his savings and loan companies. They saw enough early on to make them decide to walk away from the engagement. But the government decided that the firm should have reported what they saw, whatever that was. At least, that was their rationale for going after the firm in federal court."

"I know who you're talking about," he says.

"We helped advise the firm on communicating both in the criminal trial, which was first and covered by all the major media, and then in the civil suit that came a year later.

"It was my role to develop the communications strategy and help with talking points, although you know lawyers rarely as in never think they need anyone to tell them what to say.

"I did all the research on the media covering the criminal trial and determined who was objective and who was not. I recommended that the law firm talk first with *The Wall Street Journal*. I knew the deputy legal affairs editor and knew her to be straightforward.

"The hardest part was explaining the reason that the firm agreed to a settlement. The managing partner told me it was to get the trial, the case, and the publicity behind them. I told him they might get the trial and the case behind them, but not the publicity.

"The problem with a settlement was, and frankly to most of the public it still is, is that no matter how you explain why you took that tack, people assume you're guilty."

Petey has been rocking the beer clutched in his right hand back and forth an inch, then stops, looks at me, and drains the rest.

"I have a feeling," he says, "that despite our careers being so different, your career was in a way much like mine. It sounds as if it never got boring to you. It certainly never got boring for me, either. I enjoyed every minute."

"It was never boring," I say. We are still right at the bar, so he gets another beer as I continue to ration the Zin. "Couldn't be. Solving problems means figuring out what the problem really is, and then developing the right solution for it."

"And that," he interjects, "is what made it all so much fun."

I'm not one to have the last word on anything. But he's right.

CHapteR 7

"Did You Ever Have to Make Up Your Mind?"

A nd here I was looking forward to talking with my old friend Tom Baker, but Tom is across the room, and unsurprising to me, he is laughing so hard he has to hold his stomach.

OMG, LMAO!

Tom is, shall we say, full of himself, but not in a bad way.

"My wife has lips like a blowfish. But in a good way!"

I smile to myself. Great line from the John Travolta movie *Michael...*

Can you be full of yourself in a good way? I think maybe I am asking myself the wrong question. Or just an irrelevant one. Tom is less full of himself than he is full of life. And he brings the life out in others, too. You just can't help yourself.

"Did you ever have to make up your mind ...."

I have never been one for coincidences, yet there is one now.

Brenda Moore just walked in the room, and that song is playing. I mean, "Did You Ever Have to Make Up Your Mind" by The Lovin' Spoonful, not "When You Walk in the Room" by The Searchers. Even in retirement, long past the years of writing, speaking and advising, I gotta get the pronouns right. It never ends, this shit.

Brenda—family shortened it to "Bren"—sweeps across the room.

She is heading in my direction. It reminds me that she—

"Did You Ever Have to Make Up Your Mind" is on the playlist and the lines run through my mind … of course I remember.

Then I understand. It is not really coincidence. Just irony.

No, it is not often kind, is it?

"Nick Taylor." She is beaming, and also beaming at me. I get another hug. It is not the first from her. It is separated from its immediate predecessor by some decades.

But then, once upon a time, I had to make up my mind about two girls. It was not easy for me, and it was not kind for—

"Brenda Moore." I offer her a genuine smile. There can be shades of affectation. But not, perhaps, affection.

I see Tom Baker heading in my direction. Bren and I never did have what you would call the best of timing. He veers off.

Bren and I have only known each other since we were five in Barberton. We were shy friends at first in kindergarten. But we laughed, giggled, played, talked and more. She was my best friend, for a while.

But then I had to go and spoil it all when I came down with the biggest crush on Bren. It wasn't something you said in grade school, but basically she just wanted to be friends with me.

I had friends. What I didn't have was a girlfriend that I liked and who liked me. Why, I wondered, is this so hard. I was ten.

"All I Really Want to Do" … The Byrds … Yeah, we were friends at the start, if something more there in the middle, and once again in the end just friends. Was that all either of us really wanted to do? Irrelevant now ….

One song playing on the sound system, another playing in my head—both seem to describe my school-years relationship with Brenda Moore. It's complicated, as they say.

What the hell does that mean anyway? Just that you don't know how to explain it. And you call yourself a wordsmith.

Once in fourth grade, Cindy Brown dragged Bren over to my

desk. "I know you like her," Cindy said. "So kiss her right now."

I looked at Cindy, kind-hearted, well-meaning Cindy, who like me was obviously oblivious to how love works. Then I looked at Bren, trying to read her face and mind. She was not embarrassed or mortified. Just ... curious.

I thought that I might have had a chance with her earlier in grade school, when I was skinny. I discovered that I had a metabolism that did not permit me to eat much without gaining a lot of weight. So frequently, I just moved stuff around my plate to make it look like I was eating and tossed it out when my mom wasn't looking.

But she caught on to me, and one day said, *mister, you're going to eat everything on your plate before you can go outside again.*

Of course, I complied. As an only kid, you don't win a lot of fights in your home. You do become passive-aggressive in rebellion. Yet when I ate everything on my plate, I found that it made me feel good. Not good about myself. That was hard. Just good.

By the time Cindy marched Bren to my desk to give me what she thought was a true chance of happiness, I was chubby. No, fat.

"No," I said. "I do like her. She knows it. Apparently everybody knows it. But if she doesn't feel the same, this is not ... right."

I didn't know how else to explain it at the time. But it worked well. Bren and I stayed friends. Cindy and I stayed friends. No one else in the class gave me any crap about the incident.

Then my family moved when a new expressway threatened to take our house. I saw Bren from time to time when I went back to visit my old neighborhood. But that only lasted a year or two. New friendships had emerged, as they do.

"How are you?" She is standing close to me. "You look thinner!"

"I am a little thinner," I agree. "And ... you look lovely, Bren."

I would not say that to every woman. I would not say that to any woman. Maybe just, "you look nice."

Eddie Haskell, much? *"You look lovely today, Brenda Moore."* That is appropriate, right? Who knows, these days.

But Bren and I were always honest with each other. Given her comment on looking *thinner*, she is still honest with me.

Why then, would I change now?

She laughs and hugs me again. Class reunions feature constant catch and release. I am over my limit, but am OK with it.

"Last that I heard, you were living in Columbus."

After school, she went to Kenyon College outside Columbus, met an absolutely gorgeous guy, got married, and stayed there.

"Yes, still there. Kids and grandkids are there. Aaron and I spend some time in winter in Florida, but we're not going to move. Where are you living now? Are you still in public relations?"

Five years after my family moved, her family moved to the same school district. It was a "united" district comprising two suburbs. Hers was where the rich people lived. I had gotten to know her dad, if not so much her mom, in grade school. Nice people.

While in grade school, Bren and I were in a play about George Washington. The boys had to wear pants with the legs pulled up and tied around their knees to simulate colonial garb. I struggled to get my pants to stay put. The legs kept falling down. Suddenly, an idea, no, an epiphany, popped into my head. I could walk out on stage with my pants at their normal ankle length and announce myself as a time traveler from the future.

"George Washington, nice to meet our first president," I would say. "And the reason I appear so unusually garbed is that this is how men will dress in the year 1959. Kind of stylish, huh?"

Mr. Moore, among the parents helping out, volunteered to fix my pants. I was reluctant to let him see how fat I was, but he handled it with grace and preserved my dignity. He was always nice to me. Maybe he knew then that I had a crush on Bren. Maybe he knew more about how she felt about me than either she or I did.

Tenth grade was her first year at our school. We were not in any of the same classes. I saw her in the halls a few days after the start of the school year and knew right away that it was her.

By this time, I had shed most of the embarrassing fat. Within a week, she identified me, too. One day as school ended, she approached my locker as I stashed my books, readying for a dash to the bus.

"Hi," she said. "Do you remember me?"

My nose was stuck in my locker, but I straightened to look at her. "You're Brenda Moore."

"You remember me?!"

Like I am going to forget my first crush. "You were one of the nicest people I knew, Bren."

The Lovin' Spoonful was right again. I'd have liked her anyway ....

"We moved here over the summer."

"Bren, I'm really sorry, but I have to run because my bus is one of the first out of the lot." It was a long walk if I missed the bus.

So I closed the locker and headed past her but looked over my shoulder at her and smiled. "I think you'll like it here," I said and then was gone.

I realized later that even though I hadn't meant to be rude, I had certainly come across that way. Maybe I was not so oblivious after all.

So I sought her out next day at lunch and sat down with her. We started a conversation that lasted the entire school year, now and then over lunch, just as often before and between classes.

That prompted questions, because no one ever saw me with a girl more than a few minutes at a time.

"I see you all the time with Brenda Moore," guys would say to me, whether they were friends or not. "You going together?"

Why is the concept of a guy and a girl being friends so hard to understand?

Because most guys don't know how to do it. Mostly we talked about classes and teachers, sometimes about other students if she was curious whether they were nice or not, and here and there about events at the school or in the world.

"No, I've retired," I respond. "Just the occasional stray project."

I pause to study her face. "Most people," I finally say, "knew I was a reporter probably from the bios from the ten-year reunion. Most people still think so. You're one of the few who know otherwise."

I haven't seen her since the Twenty. Long time passing.

All of us were wandering on the dance floor talking or heading to our tables after having congregated for a photo early on at the Twenty. She was scant feet away in the middle of the floor.

"All I want to know," she said, looking at me, "is where Nick Taylor is." I had changed: bald, bearded, thin, more than any other classmate. I actually had to tell people stories about themselves before they believed I was me. She pointed at me. "You?"

Now she smiles. "I remember all our conversations. We wanted to know as much as we could about the world and the people in it."

There is something unspoken in her comment. I leave it that way.

"You? I seem to recall you as quite involved in your community, like the symphony board and other things of interest," I say.

She excitedly tells me of what proves to be a myriad interests. She is not immodest. She just wants me to know. And I am curious. She is one of the people I hoped to see, as friends since five.

"Excuse me, Bren." I smile and hold up a hand. "But you just got here and haven't had a chance to get to the bar. Can I get you a glass of wine? Yes? Red or white, then?"

I rarely saw her in the summer between sophomore and junior year, and never until I got a driver's license and could venture as far as the mall. I cruised the mall more than the drive-in.

Bren was summer help in a dress shop. If I saw her as I was wandering between record stores at either end of the mall, I'd wave a greeting. But we didn't spend any time together.

That summer was spent in misery after what I had considered a smart courtship of THAT girl over the waning months of the school year, working up the courage to ask her if she liked me, and then in recovery after she merely shook her head no. She did not even speak when she shot me down, but she might as well have told me zero, zilch, nada, not a chance in hell, buddy.

I spent a century, so it seemed, one month early that summer in my room.

"You may have retired," Bren says, "but are you still writing?"

Still writing ... I haven't written much of anything for years that wasn't related to clients, getting them out of trouble or keeping them out of trouble in "war time" when the shrapnel was flying.

In "peace time"—that is when my clients were successful and no one was shooting at them—I was successful in helping them build and burnish and then maintain a good reputation.

"No. I might have used up most of whatever creativity I had, Bren. We're devoting these first years of retirement to travel."

I guess I am breaking that bond of honesty because the truth is that I cannot bring myself to write anything. I read mysteries of all sorts: Lee Child, James Benn, Charles Todd and more.

I can't make myself read anything serious. Certainly no business books, and only occasionally any other nonfiction much less my favorite, history. I don't even read history.

"Wonderful World" ... Sam Cooke. Yeah, I smirk to myself ... I don't want to know much about nothing at all. Well, I do know something about the rise and fall.

.

STOP IT.

Oh yeah. There is one other problem with remembering every single thing like, say, Sam Cooke lyrics. That perfect memory bites back every chance it gets just to show me it is still there.

Then I tell her all this, too. I mean about being unable to be or get serious about much of anything, much less serious about writing.

"I'm not burned out," I add. "I spent decades thinking, planning, strategizing, pitching, and more. I despise chess but frankly I had to think through the first move and then the next twenty, too. It was fascinating.

"But the truth is that I don't want to think about much for a while. I want to do … nothing, really. Just travel. Maybe I am just feeling lazy right now." And then I laugh. "Feeling groovy, perhaps, if that makes any sense."

"59th Street Bridge Song" … *Simon and Garfunkel* … *Yeah, I've got to make my* retirement *last* … *ha.*

Bren smiles. "I understand. It makes perfect sense."

She and I had been friends, then almost something more. But we were always friends with benefits. Ha. That makes me smile.

That is, we were not friends with benefits as society now defines it. We enjoyed the rare benefits of understanding each other. To a naive teen largely ignored by many others, that was a benefit unlike any other. I think that applied to both of us.

Bren was the first girl I ever asked out on a date. I was the first guy ever to ask her out on a date. And I went big, too.

At the start of our junior year, I had convinced myself that based on earlier events and interactions, shall we say … that THAT girl was *never* going to like me no matter what I said or did. So I moved on. And straight in the direction of Bren Moore.

Not for the first time—or the last time—I listened to Mitch Ryder and the Detroit Wheels sing "Too Many Fish in the Sea." That summer of 1967, I told myself that there *were* a lot of fish in the sea … if I could just *catch* one.

"Incense and Peppermints" by Strawberry Alarm Clock is on the playlist as it veers into late 1967.

Bren laughs—no, actually she giggles like a school kid. "That—" she begins, but involuntarily I cut in.

"That was your favorite song. You told me."

Bren blinks twice. "We had a lot of interesting and fascinating conversations, including music," she replies. "You liked 'Soul Man,' if I recall."

Now it's my turn to laugh, somewhat in surprise.

"Yes I did, and I still love it. That will always be an absolutely great song to me. I was thinking of having it played at my funeral."

"You are not!"

"Yes, I really am."

We share a long laugh.

"I guess," she finally says, dabbing at the tears in her eyes, "that we're at the age when you think about such things."

"I guess. But meanwhile, I'm going to enjoy just being alive."

"You sound like Jack Dawson," she says. "'To making it count.'"

Usually it is men who talk in movie lines, not women. But then Bren always was a surprise. We raise our glasses, clink them together and say, "To making it count!" And we laugh again.

"What are you two up to over here?"

It is the prodigal Tom Baker.

"Tom, you remember Brenda Moore."

He has not seen her since who knows when, but gives her a hug anyway. "Of course! How are you Brenda? Stunning as always!"

Tom, Bren and I share a memory. A great one. Thanks to him.

When I went big in asking her out, it was for homecoming. I had had a hard time getting the nerve to call her for a date. So I used the cover of homecoming (back then you usually only went with a date, not by yourself or with a frenzy of friends) to call her.

If I wanted to go to the dance—the fact that I could not dance was immaterial—I needed a date. I liked her. She liked me. Why not? Bren immediately accepted. I thought that was the hard part.

Boy was I wrong.

Then I had to get her a corsage. Then I needed to know her dress color to match the corsage. Then I needed to find a flower shop. Then I needed to get us registered for homecoming because, among other preparations, the organizers made paper footballs equipped with names of all the couples attending the dance and taped them to the bleachers, assigned couples to specific tables, mimeographed programs with all our names, and more.

Bren and I were excited and exhilarated. It was so much fun.

It was Saturday, October 21, 1967. It was a momentous day in the United States, not just because it was my first date with a girl who agreed to spend the evening with me. It was a day Norman Mailer would write about in *Armies of the Night,* i.e. The MOBE.

We danced, mostly slow dances because you can sort of hide that you have no idea what to do. But I even took her out on the floor for fast dances. I was that willing to put myself out there.

I did the only move I knew from watching others, the sidestep shuffle. You know, when you move the left foot two feet left then the right foot two feet left, then go the other way. You add head and arm movements and try not to look like you're falling off a cliff.

We talked, we drank sugary punch and ate sugary treats.

I held her hand as we searched the bleacher walls not far from the tables on the gym floor, finally finding that paper football that proclaimed "Brenda and Nick."

The only time I had ever held hands with a girl was in early grade school when the teacher made us hold hands to keep us together on a field trip to a museum. This was a *lot* more fun.

But as we walked back to our table, THAT girl passed by with her date. There was an odd, mystifying look on her face, one that at the time baffled me. She looked at me for the longest time. I said hi. But Bren and I just continued back to our table.

I had made plans for dinner at an upscale restaurant. It was one of two upscale restaurants in town known for Middle Eastern food. I wanted to impress Bren, so that was my choice. My parents, who discovered the joys of eating at restaurants after church on Sunday— or rather my mother discovered the joys of not cooking after church on Sunday—loved this place.

It was one of a raft of restaurants favored by executives at the rubber companies based here—it was not unusual to have in one city a number of companies in the same industry, like say Detroit or Pittsburgh, although Akron was much smaller—and by executives who came to town from far-flung global operations.

The local economy revolved around these companies. Either you worked there or someone in your family worked there, whether in the manufacturing plants or headquarters offices. Tens and tens of thousands of families depended on these companies for their livelihoods, one reason why even into the 1970s high school graduates had readily available jobs after graduation.

One of my brothers-in-law was a longtime rubber worker. One day a tour group walked by his station. Two elderly ladies stopped in front of him. He decided to impress them with his talents. He was affixing the sidewall to a tire tread, and when finished, he rolled his right arm into the air with his hand twirling in a flourish.

The sidewall uncoiled and smacked him in the face like a lady with whom he had taken liberties. He shook his head and did it all again. The sidewall smacked him in the face once again. He stood there in a stupor when one lady said to the other, "Do you think he has to do that with every tire?"

Only one of these companies, Goodyear, retains its headquarters here. None of the others actually exists although the brands are extant - they were bought by other companies.

For its relatively modest size, Akron was then chock with steak, seafood, and ethnic restaurants. For all the executives who came to town from around the world to pay homage to headquarters, their favorite ethnic eatery was our destination for dinner.

I had made plans all right. I just had not made reservations.

Not only was our homecoming one of many at area schools that evening, but these global companies had sizable contingents from out of the country in for budget planning for the following year, something I later learned was common, and many of these had migrated to the restaurant for the evening. There was a long line.

"Do you have reservations?" the hostess asked the group of six people in front of us, all clad in homecoming finery, and they did.

I could see my evening, my life, unraveling like a sidewall tread.

"Do you have reservations?" she asked me. "No," I admitted. I had put more thought into what tie I would wear than into this. My dad suggested I make reservations, but I didn't think it necessary.

"Hey," said Tom Baker, the leader of the sextet in front of us. "They're with us. Late addition. We can squeeze them in." Tom cut my hangman's knot, untied me from the railroad tracks. I thought of a million ways he had saved my life that night.

After an hours-long dinner—Bren and I enjoyed shish kebab and I prevented the conversation from lagging by getting other people to talk about themselves—we returned to her house.

"Would you like some Clorets?" Bren fished in her purse.

"Anytime someone suggests Clorets," I said as we drove, "I make it a habit to accept. I always figure there's a reason for the offer."

We both laughed. That was about as smooth as I could be. After all, if I tried to woo a girl by saying, "Come with me to the Casbah," it was likely to come out as, "Come with me to the Cash Bar."

Yeah, well, who knows, maybe that would have worked too.

Then we had an hours-long conversation in front of the fireplace.

We talked about the MOBE, the march on the Pentagon that day, what we had heard so far on the radio.

We talked about Che Guevara, the rebel who was captured and executed earlier in the month, reportedly caught in flagrante delicto.

We talked about Vietnam. Reports were beginning to filter in about a battle, an ambush, that would be depicted as a victory— and was not—as per the book *They Marched Into Sunlight*.

We talked about music. Her favorite song was "*Incense and Peppermints*," and one of mine was "Soul Man," although there were many others in fall 1967.

We talked about the antiwar movement behind the MOBE. Joan Baez had been arrested days before, while other notables said they opposed the war but did little.

We talked about racial equality and race riots. I understand the militant and violent stance, I said, and was not surprised when she said she did too.

We talked about drugs, particularly LSD. Timothy Leary had been a cover story. Neither of us knew what to make of LSD but were skeptical about drugs.

We talked about the latest books. William Styron had been the *Newsweek* cover story for *The Confessions of Nat Turner*. Neither of us had read it yet.

She was astounded that I was so well-read. As well-read as her. Apparently no one else she knew watched so closely what was happening in the world. At least those in her fledgling circles.

"I pay attention." Ha ... another great line from Michael.

Suddenly, Mr. Moore appeared, in his robe.

"I can tell that you two are enjoying the time together," he smiled, "But it's 1:30 in the morning. Mrs. Moore and I would like to get some sleep."

I apologized profusely, that I simply did not know what time it was. And I didn't. Neither of us did.

Yeah ... I remember ... and I concluded much later it was what Mihaly Csikszentmihalyi was describing in Flow: The Psychology of Optimal Experience, *when you are so engrossed in something th*at *time does not seem to pass even as it swiftly passes ...*

"Sorry Dad," Bren said. "We were just talking about..."

"I know," he said. He smiled and retreated to the kitchen.

Bren walked me to the door. A moment of panic. It is obvious she enjoyed the evening with me. Thank you, *Newsweek*. But ....

"Danger, Danger, Will Robinson."

I had never kissed a girl before. Spin the Bottle when you're twelve doesn't count. I wasn't sure what to do. So I thought fast—

"I had a marvelous time tonight, Bren. I ... don't kiss on the first date." (Read: This is *the* first date and I don't know what to do.)

So she hugged me and said, "Me too. I hope we do it again soon."

"The Kind of Girl I Could Love" by The Monkees is on the playlist.

In 1967, Bren Moore *did* look mighty good to me ... and at least *she* was looking at *me*. Even if THAT girl was not. I listen to this song as Bren and I talk on and on, one more time.

Tom, of course, has wandered away. It is no less interesting, no less fascinating, to talk with Bren than it was all those years ago.

She is chairman of the board for the orchestra. She still runs marathons, in New York, Boston, London, and elsewhere. She owns a management consulting firm assisting female entrepreneurs.

I learn a lot about her, all of which affirms what I always knew. Bren always looked good to me, starting in 1956. I liked her. I liked being with her. She looked mighty good again in 1967.

A lifetime with her?

What an odd thought. I never thought that way then, and I refuse to permit conjecture now when it is so long after the fact.

But I knew she was the kind of girl I could love.

Thank you, Monkees.

She was just not the girl that I did love. She was not THAT girl. And there would quickly that fall come a moment to choose.

Chapter 8

Mark Laszlo is pinning his name tag to his shirt. He is alone. *"A Boy Named Sue" by Johnny Cash pops into my head.* And how could this song not claw its way to the surface? Has there ever been a song that so captured the humiliation of what it's like to be made fun of because of your name?

Yeah ... meanest thing ... he went and named me ....

Mark is wearing a Polo shirt. Nothing too out of the ordinary. But in school, he was a Carnaby Street missionary. Bell bottoms. Hip huggers. Epaulette shirts. Nehru jackets.

Nothing was too outrageous or outlandish for him to wear, which he repeatedly proved. He wasn't a rebel without a cause. He was a rebel with a clothes closet.

The biggest sensation he ever caused was at an assembly when he was among some number of students called out in front of the multitude to accept an academic achievement award. Mark wore a billowy white silk shirt—think Jerry Seinfeld, if you remember the "pirate shirt"—and gray and black striped hip huggers. There was a roar from the assembled multitude when he was introduced.

"Dedicated Follower of Fashion" ... The Kinks. Yeah, that was Laszlo all right—everything was "h.i.s." ... the coolest, hippest brand at

the time, or so we thought.

I saw him and his girlfriend at a wedding years later—Mike and Sam's in fact, in 1971—and both Mark and his date wore farmer bib overalls, and these were shorts.

When I hadn't seen that shirt for some time I asked him about it. "Spilled cherry vodka on it," he said. I believed him. But he lied because that sounded better than the truth, that he spilled grape juice on the shirt.

Mark lived next to Mike, so even if he was not in our homeroom, Mark became part of our clique. He was devastatingly smart and funny, maybe brilliant, but also strange and weird, perhaps perverse. And definitely if unthinkingly mean, even if only in pursuit of the next hilarious line. Maybe on that last one, the rest of us aren't any different.

"A Boy Named Sue" by Johnny Cash is playing in my head. Yeah, Laszlo thought it was a joke to give me a nickname, and it got the laughs he clearly intended ... which I didn't want.

Ever notice that nicknames aren't used much anymore?

When we were kids, nicknames were common. Not as common as in our parents' generation. In their era, if you were overweight, you were automatically "Tubby." Or if you had dark hair, you were "Blacky." Or if you had light hair, "Whitey."

Call anyone "Tubby" now and you would be sent to sensitivity training, if you were lucky enough to keep your job. Call anyone "Whitey," or "Blacky," and, well ... you know.

In our generation, we still used nicknames. They were not always as obvious. But they could be no less insulting or hurtful. I almost never used nicknames, and never as a pejorative. But sometimes, a nickname could be exquisitely funny and fun.

In the summer between junior and senior year, that summer of 1968, we were playing touch football at the high school stadium, having jumped the fence to gain access.

Among the TV shows we all watched was an animated version of

The Beatles, a showcase for their music, an effort to sell records. Now it was not unusual even this long after the introduction of The Beatles for teenage boys to try to affect a British accent.

Only none of us was any good at it.

Hey, Bob's your uncle ....

In the middle of this informal game, when we're all trying to sound like John, Paul, Ringo and George, Tim Baker called a timeout. Tim turned to his brother, Tom, and said with a straight face, "Who are *you* supposed to be?"

"I'm Ringo Starr."

"You don't sound like Ringo Starr."

The rest of us waited.

"You sound like some guy named Percy."

We howled and howled and howled.

The name stuck. It wasn't meant or taken as a pejorative.

Tom himself embraced the name. He even expanded it to Percival Terwilliger. But, then, he would. I called him Percy, too, for a while. But I tend to avoid nicknames.

The only time I ever assigned a nickname to anyone was to Ned ("Don't call me Ted") Kennedy and Greg Kilkenny.

Ned moved here from Boston. He loved the Red Sox. In fall 1967, I joined him in rooting for the Sox in the World Series. "I think," I told him one day, "that I'm going to start calling you Fenway." He liked it, and it stuck, too.

Greg was three inches taller than me. We played one-on-one basketball every chance we got. I had to be creative with fall-away jump shots or shoot from long range because he had a tremendous vertical leap. "I think," I told him one day, "that I'm going to start calling you Stretch. You stretch far enough to block my shot or get close enough to make me miss." He liked it, and it stuck, too.

Mark is heading toward the bar.

The first time I saw him drinking anything, it was a bottle of Mad Dog 20/20 one of the group had stolen. The last time I saw him drinking anything it was 3.2 beer—what my grandmother would call "scared water"—at the "party."

I wonder if his tastes have improved.

"A Boy Named Sue" still playing in my head. Yeah, life ain't easy for a boy nicknamed ...

I think nicknames, even if we try not to make them mean, are still often a form of bullying. I don't remember many that were not.

Tad, short for Thaddeus, Stavarsky comes to mind.

I don't see him here. Last I heard he was living in Miami, driving a pink droptop Cadillac. His parents fled Poland in the 1940s after the communists took control of the government and every facet of life. Tad, known simply as "Ski," got another name by accident.

One day he and his father were in the driveway about to get into the car when a car full of classmates drove by and at the top of their lungs they yelled, "Boner!"

In and of itself, nothing more than typical stupidity of teen boys.

But this was a word that Mr. Stavarsky apparently had not heard before. At least, he had not heard it in English.

"What are those boys saying? Are they saying 'Foreigner?'"

Tad later said he thought fast and replied, "Uh yeah, Dad. They're yelling 'Foreigner.'"

Tad avoided a conflict with his father over a word his dad might not have heard but which he probably would have shrugged off. But it was a word that was not said at all that hurt Mr. Stavarsky.

"How far do you have to go to live in peace?" he shook his head.

I never thought that incident was funny. And I never joined in when the group christened Tad as "The Foreigner."

It wasn't Tad that was bullied. It was his father. In his mind.

Somehow a nickname that made no sense at all was given to me.

Maggie Linton was a girl in our class. I really didn't know her. But in junior high, Maggie and Mark were in the same homeroom and therefore in all the same classes for three years. She liked to go by "Margo." Her father had been an army major during World War II.

I think he was in the OSS, predecessor to the CIA. Apparently, she liked to talk about her dad, "The Major."

An idea occurred to Mark. He nicknamed her, "Major Margo."

A second idea occurred to him. He nicknamed *me* Major Margo. Major Margo?

It seemed that everyone in the group knew the name before me.

"I don't understand 'Major Margo,'" I told Mark when I learned it was his handiwork. He explained the genesis of the nickname and laughed.

"But it doesn't mean anything," I responded. "I don't even know Maggie Linton."

What I did know was that it was derision. The group had turned further on me. They were outright laughing at me. The truth was that they were bullying me, although I did not think of it that way for many years and them, probably never. They'd have been surprised. It was just a joke to all of them. Some joke.

This happened late in our freshman year, spring 1966. The name stuck, although usually just shortened to "Major." Some of them called me Major throughout high school. Some forgot about it.

But as far as I was concerned, I finally knew where I stood with people that I had thought of as friends. I was a joke to them.

"Hey Major, are you going to the dance?"

"Hey Major, are you trying out for football?"

"Hey Major, did you hear that Mike Hawkins likes Sam Race?"

"Hey Major, did you hear that new song by The Beatles?"

"Hey Major, who's better, Beatles or Stones?"

Hey Major … that's all I ever heard from the group.

I did not think of revenge against the guys. I did not immediately think of leaving the group. But slowly, I began to get angry. This started coming out that spring. There were about twelve of us in the group. Sometimes others were added. One day that spring, the group assembled to hit the mall. I hitchhiked there.

We were walking to the mall when Rich Milner—a year younger

than the rest of us but was included because he was in the band formed by Mike Hawkins—started giving me shit. I fought back with words. And I literally got in his face.

"I have to take this shit from these guys," I yelled. "But you're just a stupid eighth grader and I am not taking any shit from you."

Mike could see the escalation—I was about to swing at Rich — and he moved to put a stop to the jawboning before it become violent.

"Knock it off! We're supposed to be in the same group here."

Same group. Same group.

I glared at Mike.

Same group that makes fun of me.

I am about done with this same group. You are not my friends.

But I was not yet confident enough, tough enough, to leave the group, to turn my back on the group: the in-crowd of our class. There was cachet, after all, attached to membership in this group.

Mark orders a beer and like everyone else who talks to the bartenders before classmates, looks around. I look away.

I did not see the group much that summer. None of them lived in our allotment. The group stopped by my house once to check in on me, en route home from a local lake—a swimming hole, really.

Usually in summers, I spent every day at this park: a small lake with four docks out in the deep end of the lake. And I probably would have met the group there that day. But I had a bad case of poison ivy. Until it abated, I just stayed in the rec room in the basement and listened to music.

I was stunned they would stop to see me. I was even more stunned to find that I really did not care that they would stop to see me. I was getting angrier every day.

It even occurred to me that I could be a hitman for the mob, a sniper in the service, and it might not bother me.

But the thought that it might not bother me bothered me.

I remained in the group throughout the first half of our sophomore year, although I had begun to put a little distance between us.

Then came the party at my house. The party even seniors talked about as legendary. Senior boys, stars of the sports teams, would see me and then talk to each other, and nod at me. Senior girls, untouchable to sophomores, would see me, whisper and giggle.

The party that people talked about for the rest of high school as legendary. And in the spring of both junior and senior years, the party that had people asking me if I was going to do it again.

"Do It Again" ... Beach Boys ... the new No. 1 now in my head.

"The party of the century, Major. Do it again!"

That would be no. We were all lucky to survive the first one.

Mark is looking at me now.

Starting the year before, when I was a freshman, my parents would decamp Ohio for two weeks in Florida. It was a trial run for moving there every winter when they retired some years later.

My grandmother was nominally my babysitter. She had lived on farms most of her life and still went to bed not long after the sun went down. Two factors militated in favor of permitting me more or less free rein of the house, to come or go, as I pleased.

First, she never woke up at night. Ever. Second, she had no clue as to the foolishness of which teen boys were capable. None.

I told her that I was having a few friends over to spend the night Friday. There were more who showed than had been invited. I had heard many drinking tales from the guys. They could drink any beer, wine, or whiskey, put away endless bottles of high-powered alcohol, get drunk without ever getting sick. It was my turn.

"Welcome to the Majors, Mr. Hobbs." Yeah ... makes me smile just thinking about it even now ....

It wasn't as if I had never drank before. Frankie Mecklenberg, a kid in our neighborhood, used to raid the liquor cabinet at his house, usually to steal vodka to make screwdrivers for us.

And then, too, my mom worked with legions of secretaries at one of the rubber companies, and frequently was invited to weddings by her coworkers. She rarely attended the weddings but usually made the receptions, with me in tow.

Sometimes my dad made it, too, if he wasn't working. But at that time—in the Sixties and into the Seventies at least until the first Arab oil embargo—overtime and extra shifts were plentiful.

During that 1966-67 school year, there seemed to be an almost preternatural number of weddings and receptions that my mom, apparently not trusting me out of her sight, made me attend.

Turned out she couldn't trust me in her sight either.

One of her secretary friends from work was a little old lady named Alice, who turned me on to 7 and 7—that is, Seagram's 7 Crown and 7 Up—which then was always served at receptions.

Alice also introduced me to a pretty girl named Carol Forbes, and I worked up the courage to ask her to dance once a slow dance finally played. Only, turned out it wasn't a slow dance.

I was mortified when suddenly the tempo kicked up. Carol knew the moves. I did not. She stopped, then smiled.

"You can't dance, can you?" she said. I admitted as much.

"I thought it was a slow dance," I explained.

"OK," she said. "Let's go sit down and talk until a slow dance comes around again."

She didn't call me an idiot. She didn't roll her eyes.

Carol Forbes was pretty. She was intimidating in the way that pretty girls can be to us guys. I wasn't the only guy there, but I was the first guy to ask her to dance, and that was at least fifteen minutes after the band started playing dance songs.

We sat and talked and then danced to the slow songs. I learned that fortune favors the bold, as they say. I could get a pretty girl to dance with me, and talk with me, too.

"Pretty Ballerina" by the Left Banke replaces "Do It Again" as the new No. 1 rattling around in my head as I avoid Mark. Yeah ... I did ask her for this dance ... and yes, she did oblige me ... and I hadn't even had a 7 and 7.

Good Lord ... does anyone have a playlist in their head like me? I can pick any week in any year at least from 1965 to 1975 and spin the platters ....

Bartenders at receptions never told me I was too young to drink, they just poured. And I told my mom I was drinking Seven-Up. I consumed a lot of seven and sevens that school year.

"Bottle of Wine" by the Fireballs replaces "Pretty Ballerina" in my head now, and just as quickly "Sugar Shack," the only other big hit for the Fireballs rollicks through my mind.

Seriously?

I also learned that if you successfully make it to your bed at the end of the night, you do not dare close your eyes right away.

Just lie there for a while and look at the ceiling; sooner or later you'll nod off. If you close your eyes right away, well, you might or might not make it to the bathroom in time. Trust me.

I learned how much I could drink at any one time by learning how much I could *not* drink at any one time.

I heard ad nauseam from the guys in the group that they could drink ad infinitum. It turned out they could only drink ad nausea.

Tom Baker, Mark Laszlo, Tad Stavarsky, Chuck Williams, Frankie Mecklenberg and Sam Bradford showed. I was just getting to know Tom, but he was key: he had a driver's license and I only had my temps. I didn't know Sam but knew of him. I knew Chuck from band. Both were juniors. Frankie was not just a friend from the neighborhood. He was also brother to THAT girl.

At dusk, the guys loaded into our 1959 Ford, which, with a 332 cubic inch engine, was a beast. I backed out of the driveway without the lights, a testament to our nosy neighbors.

We ... were ... in ... search ... of ... *beer.*

Frankie knew the bars in all the suburbs and suggested we try two bars on the west side of Barberton, not far away. At the first, the fake ID didn't work. But it did at the second and yielded two cases of 3.2% beer. I'm not sure 3.2% beer is even made any more. By the way, studies have labeled 3.2% beer as a "non-intoxicating beverage."

Yeah, maybe if you're grown up and used to drinking ...

We headed to a secluded spot and opened up the case. It was a learning experience for me.

I don't mean the beer. I mean the people.

Suddenly, everyone was different. Guys swigging beers, wiping the backs of their mouths with their hands like they saw in movies. Guys extolling the virtues of drinking beer, getting drunk.

It wasn't the first time I'd gone drinking with a bunch of guys.

I'd gone several times with Frankie, a couple of times with a group of busboys from a restaurant where I had worked summer of 1966 and then with other groups including Dave Canterbury and Larry Bloom from the neighborhood, in Dave's brother's 1961 Ford.

That time, we just had a six pack. Dave, Larry and Frankie wondered how we could get more. As it turned out, that was plenty.

We parked in a cemetery and drank the ubiquitous 3.2% beer. It was the same sort of response, at least at the start, about how much fun it was to drink. Except that Larry threw up on the floor of the back seat, and he hadn't even got through half a beer.

Then a police car came in the other entrance. Dave drove out at the same speed as the cop car came in, with lights out. Nobody finished their beers. I wonder if the others would have anyway.

But nobody panicked. The beers weren't tossed out until after we left the cemetery and the headlights were back on. That should have been a tip off about the difference between what guys *say* they do and what they *actually* do.

Now that we had our booty, Tom and I stayed in the car while the others congregated behind the car, all of us proclaiming how good the beer was when in fact it was shitty.

After everyone had one beer, or tried to look like it, we thought this place was too exposed and so decided to take the car home and then take the beer to a nearby golf course to finish the case. Everyone was right behind the car except Frankie. He was taking a leak in the field at the side of this remote road.

"Taylor," Tom whispered. "Start the car and take off. We'll see if the others can catch us." Hey, be really stupid? Sure, why not.

I started the car, waited a few seconds, and then punched the accelerator. The car didn't move. I was still in park. Everyone ran to the doors and jumped into the car just as I shifted into drive.

Frankie zipped up and sprinted to the car as we started to move. I was so excited about this prank that I forgot to close my door.

Frankie reached the car and the open door. He held on to the door. His feet were moving a mile a minute as the car—tires initially spinning on the loose gravel on this back road—got traction. But he couldn't get in the car. We were going too fast for him to try. And the only door open was mine and I occupied the seat.

Tom and I started to panic. "Stop the car!" Tom yelled.

Instantly, I punched the brake. Frankie hit the door as we stopped and crumpled to the ground. He hit the door so hard that the hinges were knocked out of place, and there was a crack in the window.

Frankie lay in a heap. He wasn't moving. Everyone was stunned. "Oh my God!" Sam yelled. "You killed him."

I got out of the car. "Frankie, Frankie! Are you all right?"

Oddly though, the first thought I had was that this act ought to go over real well with his sister, THAT girl. It doesn't matter she doesn't *like* her brother. I couldn't very well ever expect to get anywhere with her if I *killed* her brother.

Frankie groaned, opened his eyes and grinned. "You son of a bitch," he said. "You were going to leave me here, weren't you?!"

I am still rationing the Zin at my station near the bar. Mark looks as if he is about to speak to me but is interrupted before he can even start.

"Hey, Laszlo," says Mike. "There's a bunch of us from the old neighborhood over here catching up. Jay Harris, Linda Leonard and some of the others. C'mon over."

Mark and Mike move away.

After I nearly killed Frankie, we all went back to my house and dropped off the car. The door closed but just barely, and already I worried about the response when my parents came home. How will I explain this? I'm dead meat.

"We're not taking the beer into the house," I announced. "But we can take it with us to the golf course and drink the rest of it there."

We trooped to a nearby golf course, drinking along the way, and then we drank a little more. We really hadn't consumed much alcohol; this was low-wattage beer and in pretty small bottles.

By now there were two groups, Tom, Tad, Mark and me, and Sam, Chuck and Frankie, spread on different greens. Chuck and Sam were juniors and knew each other well. Sam and Frankie sat next to each other in a few classes and were friends too.

Next thing I know, it's just Tad and me. Tom and Mark are gone. We haven't heard anything from the others for a while.

***

"Hey Taylor!" Tom is yelling at me from across the room. "We're getting the football team together over here to tell some lies. Get a beer and come on over."

I nod but I do not move just yet, lost in thought over Laszlo, Major Margo, and the legendary party.

***

"Taylor?" Stavarsky was talking to me as we lay on the green. "You seem to have your act together. How do you do it?"

What was he talking about? I didn't have anything together.

"I want to know why God hates me," he said. It occurred to me that he was talking to himself. "God shit on me. I never get anything to go my way. I never get a break for just me."

I wait a few seconds and then respond.

"Tad, I doubt God hates you. But I will tell you this, Tad: if you want anything to go your way, if you want to get the breaks to go your way, then you need to do it yourself. Don't wait on God, and don't count on anyone else either. Do it yourself." I could hardly believe the words coming out of my mouth.

My first thought was, am I talking to him, or to myself?

My second thought was, I've heard this lament from Tad about God shitting on him before, and I didn't want to hear it again.

Suck it up, bud, I thought, and stop complaining.

"Tad, I don't know where Tom or Mark are, and I have no idea where the other guys are either. I need to make sure everyone is all right. Let's go make sure they're all OK."

We overtook the wandering Mark on the walk back to my house. We found Tom collapsed on the front porch. He was trying to talk to us, but he was at best inarticulate. He could only groan.

"Beer, please." I thank the bartender and head over to the guys who were on the football team to tell old stories.

***

"Tom," I said, "where are the other guys? Where are Chuck and Sam and Frankie?" I got Tad, Mark, and Tom into the house and got some food into each of them. I drank as much as them, or as much as they said they did, but I was feeling all right. What's with these guys?

"Tom, tell me, where are the others?"

"I think," he mumbled, "they said something about The Castle."

"The Castle? You're kidding, right?"

"Yeah, The Castle. I think they were going to hitchhike there."

Great.

These guys told their parents they're staying at my house. If they ended up dead or arrested, whichever comes first, I was going to be in deep shit, first with their parents, and then with mine. Explaining the car already was bad enough.

The Castle was an old barn turned into a dance club in the next township. There were Friday night battle of the bands competitions. I had never been there.

I stuffed Tad, Mark, and Tom into the '59 Ford with the bum door, and we headed out. I hoped we wouldn't see a cop on the way.

We arrived without incident. Tom volunteered to find the

missing members. But I gave him instructions.

"Tom," I said, "here's what I want you to tell these guys. They can come with us back to my house right now. Car is right here. Or they can stay here and find their own way home. Then they can explain to their parents how they ended up here. You tell them that I'm covered, because I can just say they left and I didn't know where they were going."

Mark and Tad want to go too. I say no.

"You're staying put," I said. There was no argument. I felt something I had rarely felt before: Power. No, control. No, both.

Five minutes later, Tom emerged with the others.

"What the hell were you guys thinking?" I said.

They all laughed. "Well, we just thought it would be fun."

Yeah. Some fun. Getting killed or getting arrested. Some fun. And if you managed to get through the night you'll face house arrest for the rest of your lives when your parents find out.

***

"Hey Taylor." Tom welcomes me to the football boys. "Tell everyone why in the picture of the team in '68, you, me and Buck Jones are the only ones laughing. We're supposed to look mean."

It was late before I had everyone back in the corral. I brought out more food for all of us, assembled in the rec room in the basement. Chips, dips, pretzels. Your basic munchies.

Everyone was talking about how much they had to drink, how much fun this had been, how we have to do it again next year.

I went upstairs to get more food. When I returned, I saw a sight that stunned me and which I hoped never to see again.

"Hey Major," Laszlo said. "Look at me."

Mark had taken off all his clothes. He had affixed a mousetrap to his private parts. Everyone else was giggling like little kids. I couldn't tell if they thought this was funny or were embarrassed.

"Laszlo," I said. "That is just plain perverted. Get that mousetrap off your dick now. You give the mice in this house a bad name."

"I don't know what I'm doing," he said. But he removed the mousetrap. "I'm drunk."

"You're not that drunk," I said. "That is just plain perverted."

What I was thinking, though, was, *I know how much you and everyone else drank. And it wasn't that much. We had to throw away a lot of that case of beer. You're not drunk. You just want to be drunk.*

It was after midnight by the time the conversation slowed, after the others had finished reliving the highlights of the evening. I hadn't said much, partly because I was worried about the car, partly because I was learning how much we all lie. I had spent most of the night listening to the rest of them create a legend.

Bullshit, it turns out, is a lot like work. It expands to fill the space allotted to it, only that space is infinite:

The number of cases of beer consumed was quintupled.

The number of guys who were there doubled to fourteen.

The number of girls with us expanded from none to twenty-eight.

You know, *two girls for every boy.* Thank you, Jan and Dean.

Apparently I had even hired a band to play for the evening.

What was at best a sleepover is now the best party any of these guys have ever attended. Even if it was never a party.

***

"The reason Tom and I are smiling," I explain, "is that for the picture, us seniors are sitting in the front row with our legs crossed and our helmets in our laps, and everyone else is standing in the back row. And Buck is right behind us, whispering, "Taylor, Taylor. I gotta pee. I'm going to pee in your helmet."

All of us old men laugh and laugh as if we have never heard this before—or at least not since the last reunion.

***

I finally got the guys herded to the bedrooms upstairs. By then we were all exhausted, so we were all quiet. I told them to stay that way. But of course it wasn't over yet. Just when I think everyone is in bed,

I get in bed too. And then ....

"Taylor." It's Tad. "I had a little accident."

Great. Now what?

Tad had barfed in the bathroom, most in the toilet, some not. Worse, while he was trying to stick his head in the toilet to throw up, there was another little surprise coming out the back end. It was a perfect little round turd, now sitting right in the middle of the pink throw rug in front of the toilet.

"Oops," he said. "It came out both ends."

"All right," I said. "It happens. I'll clean up the barf."

I have a strong stomach. This is useful later because my wife cannot handle anything (if the kids would barf, she would barf). It was almost always me taking care of the kids until they were done hurling whatever had been their last meal.

"But you clean up that turd."

"OK," Tad said meekly, contritely. We both get to work. "I'm really sorry I messed up your bathroom."

The next morning was without incident. My grandmother actually made pancakes for everyone. If she heard anything at all during the night, she was never going to tell. I doubt she heard us at all.

Mark was the last one to be picked up.

"Hey Dad," he said when his father arrived. "We were goofing around and messed up the driver side door. Can you take a look and see if you can fix it for us?"

Mr. Laszlo was a lot like Mr. Baker. He remembered being young. He took a two by four, wedged it into the hinges, and popped the door right back into place. My thanks were profuse.

"Glad to help," he grinned. "But no more shenanigans, boys."

Mark grinned too, and waved as they drove away.

I explained away the cracked window without difficulty. "Dad, I was washing the car so it was clean when you got home, and I tripped, with the metal nozzle cracking the glass as I struggled to keep my balance."

Sounded plausible, to me anyway. I'm still not sure my dad believed it, or just didn't want to know.

By Monday, everyone in the school, across every grade, knew about the "party." The party was a legend. So was I. Even if it never happened.

I learned that we will all tell as many lies as necessary to make ourselves feel good about ourselves and look good to others. What is truth is often held hostage to ego, and therefore to reputation. Who we are sometimes is not enough for our ego, so we lie.

Were any of these guys drunk? I didn't think so. You had as much chance of getting drunk on 3.2 beer as getting bit by a shark in Lake Erie.

But if you *wanted* to be drunk ....

Yeah, I was a legend all right. And I was still Major Margo.

But that wouldn't be the case for long, because now I knew the truth: all the tales these guys had been telling about all the things they had done, these were things apparently only I had done.

Everybody lies now and then, or all the time. Everybody lies.

I had also learned that night another valuable lesson. Everybody is more willing to follow than to lead. Maybe it was because we were in my house and in my car that I felt I could be—or maybe should be—the one in charge, and I did take charge.

***

After the football boys have disbanded to talk to others, Tom and I head to the appetizer table. Mark Laszlo is there.

"A Boy Named Sue" ... again at the top of the charts in my head.

What will Mark and I say if we talk to each other?

Hey, Major, remember the party at your house? Hey, Major, remember the pirate shirt I wore? Hey, Major, remember the nickname I gave you? Hey, Laszlo, it doesn't matter much to me...

Mark is crunching on a carrot but looks up at me.

"A Boy Named Sue" ... Johnny Cash ... louder in my head. Hey ... how ... do ... you ... ... now ... you ... gonna ....

"Nick Taylor," he smiles. "It's good to see you, my friend."

CHapteR 9

Tom and I hit the appetizer table, and it is quite a spread. Betty Janes— also known simply as Betty Jane—is the first person we see there.

"Hi guys," she looks up from the food. "How've you been?" She knows Tom—everybody knows Tom—but squints at my name tag, just to be sure. Almost nobody recognizes me. I don't know who traveled the farthest to get here tonight, but if there were a prize for who changed the most, it'd be me.

Betty Janes was a pretty and vivacious classmate. I didn't know her well, but knew she was game for just about any joke or prank or hijinks in school. Apparently, long afterward, too.

"Doing great, Betty," I say. "How about you? I met your daughter once," I continue, "at the bank branch where she was a teller. She looks like you. Nice young lady."

Tom looks at me, and I know what he is thinking.

At the Twenty, the festivities were spread over two nights. Sort of like how birthdays for kids now are spread over days or weeks. That Friday night, we met at a drive-in that still is hugely popular, and nationally renowned. Jimmy Buffett allegedly wrote "Cheeseburger in Paradise" after eating at this drive-in before a performance at a nearby tour stop for all major artists. Who knows?

Friday night was classmates only. Not that my wife would have gone, but she was supremely pissed off not to have the choice.

Then we convened at a winery owned by an alum to continue the festivities until late. I went home after several hours, but the party, it seemed, continued long afterward elsewhere.

Tom told me later about a dozen or so classmates went skinny dipping at a pond on the east side of our township that once was open for swimming but now is surrounded by apartments.

So Tom and Bill Conrad are treading water and drinking beer, when Betty swims by them. All, of course, buck naked.

Tom turns to Bill and says, "There goes Betty Janes, one of the sexiest girls in our class. Twenty years ago we'd have been in hot pursuit. Now, we're just trying to keep our beer dry."

No matter how many times I tell my wife I wasn't skinny dipping—and it really was Bill Conrad and not me out there in the buff—she still suspects I was treading water, drinking beer and, as the old song goes, watching all the girls go by. It's not true.

1. The Girl Most Likely to Go Skinny-Dipping with Classmates. *Not this again. I hate* listicles. *Well, shit, then, here we go ....*

"The 10 People You Meet at Your High School Reunion."

Ha. Nailed it. Thank you, Betty Janes. No, really. Betty Janes just has to be at the top of this list. Who's next?

Ken Barrett is loading his plate with tofu, somewhere in the middle of the appetizer table. He pauses and looks at Tom and me.

"Hey man," he says to both of us. "S'up." We both nod.

"Ken, how they hanging?" Tom says.

"Dude," is all I say. Given his appearance, it is appropriate.

We chat a bit, the usual pleasantries. Are you still working? Do you still live in the area? It was not a long conversation.

Ken was the first hippie in our area. Chances are, he is the lone holdout left, sort of like the Japanese soldiers found in jungles decades after World War II ended, still fighting the good fight.

Most baby boomer men have what I call the "boomer beard." That is, a "circle beard." You know, a moustache that circles down to a small beard on your chin. I didn't make this up. It's popular, especially for bald guys like me. Almost a part of the uniform.

Not Ken. Full beard. Long hair.

If he looked in the mirror, he would see Tom. Same thing. Full beard, long hair. But Tom doesn't live in conservative middle America. He lives in a land of eternal snow and sun and chic.

Ken was the first guy to tell me he had had sex with a girl. We were 15. Not that he often confided in me. I was astounded. We just happened to be at a wedding reception in the summer of 1966. His dad and my mom worked in the same office and were invited by a coworker to attend the wedding of his daughter. Ken and I were the only teen-age boys there each other knew.

He bragged about these sexual conquests and other myriad exploits. I only talked with him for a few minutes when I decided there were better uses for my time, like looking for a 7 and 7.

Ken also was the first guy in our class to get arrested for pot. Pot arrests (not so sure about pot *use*) were so unusual at the time—that was also in 1966—that there was even a story about his arrest on the front page of the "metro" section in the newspaper.

My mom said his dad was completely humiliated.

I think Ken still owns a head shop. Wonder if he sells CBD.

2. The Guy Most Likely to Smoke a Joint in the Parking Lot.

Nailed it. Ken the stoner is heading for the door right now. So who's next on the list? ....

John Norris is waiting at the end of the appetizer line. He is noisily chomping on a massive piece of broccoli, no dip, no dressing. He was never one to be self-conscious, just fully self-aware.

He lights up when he sees me. I'm not sure he knows Tom.

"Nick Taylor!" We do the guy hug. He shakes hands with Tom.

John looks a lot like Sir Richard Branson, or maybe I should say, Sir Richard Branson looks a lot like John Norris. Longish blond hair, neatly trimmed circle beard, perpetual grin.

For a while, mostly in late grade school and early junior high, John and I were good friends. I learned a lot from John. He was the first person I knew who didn't care what other people thought of him. He was too busy with what was important to him.

John was brilliant. He was also the first person I ever saw carry a briefcase to school. That would be junior high and high school.

John was not just a *brain*. He was also adventurous. I guess that's how you describe yourself as a teen, when you're pushing 70. At the time, though, when you're doing all this stupid stuff that teens do, especially boys, you just think it's fun.

Yeah, it's a wonder any of us made it out alive ....

John lived in the country. He built a helicopter with a go-cart frame that he stored under a tarp behind the barn. He built a speedboat that he stowed in the boathouse at property his family owned on Portage Lakes, a chain of lakes south of downtown Akron.

At the time, despite the encroachment of housing "allotments" or developments, there were a considerable number of houses set on gargantuan acreage on the west side of our township. The helicopter never caused any trouble for John. He would fly it to see other people—of course they had to be out in the country too—and now and then take me along.

That was summer 1964, and it did impress the girls, although John seemed oblivious. I wasn't, but didn't know what to do about it.

I knew he was different because he managed to get a Norden bombsight, took it apart, and put it back together again. I talked him out of using it to drop water balloons from his helicopter.

It was the speedboat that almost got us killed in the summer of 1965. Also almost arrested. Actually, spending any amount of time with John, it was sort of like which would come first.

John and I were out on the lakes one day when he opened it up full throttle, racing around the series of interconnected lakes and creating huge wakes that rocked other boats on the water. For most guys, it would have been simple fun. For John, anything but a normal guy, it was a science experiment.

He had tuned up the homemade engine and wanted to be sure it worked properly, apparently at very high speeds. I don't know if someone complained to the county sheriff, or if there just happened to be a sheriff patrol boat out at the same time. But all of a sudden, there was a boat with flashing lights closing fast.

We were at the closed end of one lake, which was separated from another by a causeway on which ran the raised roadway. The patrol boat was between us and the bridge that connected the two lakes, 100 yards behind the deputies. The bridge arched twenty feet above the water line and through which boat traffic ran.

But there was a smaller concrete bridge behind us which at three feet above the water line clearly was not designed for boat traffic, but connected the causeway to the mainland about ten feet away.

We were trapped. At least, I thought we were, and undoubtedly so did the deputies in the boat. But not John. He was doing calculations on the height of the bridge and the height of the speedboat.

"If I get in trouble," he said to me out of the corner of his mouth, still looking at the small bridge, "I might not get into Harvard."

"You're not thinking about—"

Suddenly the speedboat roared as we made for the tiny bridge. "When we get there," John said, "duck to the bottom, NOW!"

We screamed—literally, in my case—through the opening, both of us on the bottom of the boat, with about three inches to spare.

The patrol boat had to circle back to the main bridge, hung up momentarily by other boat traffic. By the time the deputies emerged into the interconnected lake, John had put in to the boat garage and closed the door.

We were safe. We were alive. We were scared shitless.

I never went boating with him again.

It's all I can do not to laugh about this as I talk with John.

As we moved deeper into junior high school I didn't hang around much at all with John, just now and then. John was not in any group except science club. I did not stop hanging with him because I thought I might get killed by doing so, whether by land or sea or air. Rather, he started spending all his time in what he called R&D, tinkering, experimenting, inventing.

And he did go to Harvard, and then MIT.

John invented numerous algorithms, capturing attention along the Route 128 "tech valley" around Boston, and made serious money. He is now a serial entrepreneur.

John did not show up to show off. He came to see old friends. And I enjoyed every minute of the conversation with him.

3. The Guy Most Likely to Quietly Underwrite the Reunion

That was in keeping with John Norris: share the wealth with his classmates and make it more affordable to come.

Yeah … no wonder this appetizer spread is so good … think I'll have me some more shrimp.

Who's next?

Lou Janssen is juggling his whiskey glass and his appetizer plate. He puts the whiskey down long enough to load more on the plate and then picks up the glass to move to the next appetizer.

I am surprised to see him. I am not surprised at how he looks.

Lou, who I knew had been a chief executive officer of a Fortune 500 company, stepped out of the digital pages of GQ to be here. Italian sports jacket, a beige cotton unlined blazer that looks to me to be maybe Mariano Rubinacci and 850 Euros, crisp blue shirt of the uniform that corporate executives prefer, and jeans.

Lou slows his progress to look at our name tags, which to me immediately suggests he is determining if we are worth his time.

The real question is, is he worth ours?

His father was an executive who used his affluence to move the family to the rich suburb that comprised half of our united school district, because our schools were so highly rated. That was just before senior year.

Lou didn't make many friends. He was a jerk. I am being kind.

He was full of himself, with the kind of undeserved and unchecked arrogance that must be supported by belittling other people.

"Gentlemen," he says, as if addressing the board of directors.

I got to know him because he made the basketball team, whose captain, Kev Bennett, was a friend of mine and introduced us.

When we first played pickup ball, Lou razzed me to see how Kev would respond, knowing we were friends. When Kev didn't say anything, Lou accelerated from razzing to ridiculing me.

I took it for a few times when we played, then finally had enough. "You may be new here," I said. "But you're an asshole." I walked off the court despite the entreaties of others to stay. I did play in other pickup games with him throughout senior year of high school and freshman year in college when he was in town.

But he was better behaved in those subsequent games. When someone calls you an asshole to your face, you don't know how they'll respond the next time you see them.

Still, when his dad died while we were freshmen in college in early 1970, I went to calling hours. I felt bad for Lou. There weren't many classmates there from our school or the one from which he transferred. Hard to care what happens to an asshole.

"Still living here in town?" Is it a question, or a challenge?

"I do," I say. "I've lived elsewhere particularly when working on newspapers. But my wife and I decided to come home."

Tom looks at Lou, and I can tell he is trying to decide whether this is worth his time. "Park City," is all he says.

Lou seems impressed. "What do you in Park City?"

I feel ignored. Hometown must be boring. But Tom responds.

I could look around and signal boredom or contempt or anger. I do not. I watch their faces as Tom explains his work as a coach. Both of us know Lou is waiting for us to ask about him. But I know his career because he worked at companies that were competitors with some of my clients at the public relations firm.

Lou became a financial whiz and eventually chief financial officer for one of the largest companies in the Midwest. When the incumbent CEO left for another job, Lou was named chief executive officer.

He was successful in building the company, but he also built a reputation as ruthless. Even in the corporate stratosphere, being called a son of a bitch means it is much worse than that.

In fact, being called an SOB means people think you're a jerk. But actually being *called* a son of a bitch, that says people really mean it. The board eventually asked him to leave after what is known in the corporate arena as a "Come to Jesus" meeting.

Lou joined a PE group in New York and was added to the boards of a number of companies because of his experience.

"Sounds interesting, Tom," he smiles. "And it sounds as if you've made a difference for these kids." He turns to me.

"I know you were in public relations, Nick," he says. "I knew from the CEO at our main competitor that you were successful in getting him on CNBC, or in *The Wall Street Journal* for example. I told him I was envious and asked him who his PR guy was and he said you. I knew it was the same guy I knew in high school.

"Are you still working at that agency? I heard it was a great firm for investor relations, media relations and crisis management. But I let my head of corporate communications make his own choices. Or if you're retired, are you doing any freelance work?"

Who are you and what have you done with Lou Janssen?

"I'm retired. There are other things I want to do now." I study his face for a moment. "You're still full of surprises, Lou."

"In a good way?" He sips his whiskey.

"Yes," I smile. "In a good way."

We all laugh, put down our plates, and clink glasses. Now I know why he is here. He must make amends.

4. The Asshole Most Likely to Have Finally Grown Up.

Nailed it ... oh yeah. "Don't stop him, he's on a roll." Ha. I smirk privately at that line from Animal House ... but as Satchel Paige once said, ain't bragging if it's true.

Who knows what finally prompted Lou to stop being an asshole. Getting fired might have something to do with it. But whatever it was, the change is for the better. He is actually interesting.

Tom has wandered off again. Big surprise; he always did know more people than me. But then once I started dating THAT girl, most of my time was spent with her.

She was a lot more fun than the guys... or anyone else.

As the reunion rolls on, I talk with a raft of classmates. Some, not many, I seek out at their tables when I recognize them. But some, once they know who I am, seek me out at the bar table I have commandeered or when they stop at the bar for a refill.

I learned as a reporter to command the high ground. That is, find a spot from where you can observe the crowd and its actions, its temperament, its movement. I still follow this strategy.

Jon Farage stops at the bar, identifies me and stops to chat. Jon is a standup comedian in his spare time. Actually, he is a salesman at a company manufacturing materials for use in aerospace and automotive applications.

But he is funny, sometimes hilarious, and has been featured on some of the late-night shows and has served as an emcee for black tie events run by big non-profit organizations.

I like Jon, but he can be over the top. At the Twenty, when so few classmates could recognize me, Jon as the emcee joked that I was what all the guys could look forward to. Very funny. How about a drum roll, too.

Yeah, drop the mic, Jon. Please. Random thought: should I put Jon on my Thrillist list? Nooooo-OH-ooooo! Ok so well, then, who's next ....

Ned Kennedy is heading straight to the appetizers, or is it to me?

It really is amazing, all the people he met, all the things he did, trying to save the world.

Yeah, there aren't enough people like Ned Kennedy.

There was never any artifice or ambiguity attached to Ned. He was always straight with everyone, about everything.

For example, his name was actually Edward M. Kennedy, and while he professed to admire that unrelated family, he did not want to be called Ted, so it was Ned.

Seeing him reminds me of when I saw *Forrest Gump*, I laughed to myself because it was *so* Ned Kennedy. Ned had an IQ more than double the fictional Forrest, but ended up in just about every major event of the late Sixties too.

"Nick Taylor!"

Ned is grinning, and I am laughing.

"It's me! Ned Kennedy! You know, Fenway?" He is standing with arms askew, as if they are the wings of a plane banking toward landing, in the proverbial "ta-da" pose. "And you know what, Nick, the Red Sox are finally winning World Series championships!"

We both laugh.

"Yeah," I say, "now if we can just get the Tribe ..."

And we laugh again.

I have not seen Ned since June 1970. After Kent State.

He is completely unselfconscious about hugging me, and I think that it must be an east coast thing because in the midwest, guys will hug but they are not quite sure about it.

Yeah ... probably just me.

I think I've hugged as many men as women now. As much as I had steeled myself for hugging people, I still shiver.

Yeah, times have sure changed: hugging men is acceptable, less so hugging women. Me, I don't want to hug anybody.

I was always impressed by Ned. He was a man of the world. Or maybe he was just a teen of the world, but I didn't know anyone else our age who did what he did.

Three examples ....

First, Ned went to Haight Ashbury in The Summer of Love. His dad was an executive at one of the rubber companies in Akron and traveled for sales meetings. When he went to San Francisco in August 1967, he asked Ned if he wanted to see Haight Ashbury.

Ned was impressed with what he saw starting with The Diggers, a group of community activists that made available free food, clothing and more at stores set up around Haight Ashbury.

"I talked to some of The Diggers, and they were cool," Ned said later. "They really seem to want to help people, help everyone. I heard them say things that made a lot of sense, like 'do your own thing' and 'today is the first day of the rest of your life.'"

He walked through the Panhandle, an area around Golden Gate Park full of fields and flowers, where he observed thousands of people gathered to sing, play ... and more.

Ned told me that at first he thought Haight Ashbury was "groovy." He began to see it differently when he walked through the area with his father, who showed him how to analyze what he saw.

Many people in the streets were ragged, hungry, and stoned. They were in the streets because they lived in the streets. I knew from *Newsweek* that Governor Ronald Reagan had said of hippies, "They dress like Tarzan, have hair like Jane, and smell like Cheetah." What Ned said made me wonder what was true.

Many shops popped up, some in the days Ned and his dad were there, selling jewelry, clothes and other "hippie" material and no longer was it free. People he had seen taking free clothes at the Diggers store, he now saw selling those clothes on the street.

"Sounds like Jesus and the Moneychangers at the Temple," I said when Ned told me about the creeping capitalism.

"What?"

I tried to explain how Jesus threw out the people making money from those who went to the temple to worship.

"When you look at people or places," his dad told him, "don't just look, but also see. Ask yourself, what is it you *really* see?"

I was surprised when Ned told me that it was fascinating, but not for all the reasons we all thought. When his dad challenged him to analyze what he thought he saw, Ned started asking questions.

The Diggers were brutally honest—crime, particularly rape, had begun to proliferate along with drug sales and usage.

"You know at the start, we felt we were making a sincere difference for the community," one Digger told him when he visited one of their stores. "Then it started changing.

"People started coming here from all over because they heard about it or read about it and at first that was groovy, you know. But now a lot of the people coming here seem to want to cash in on this scene. It isn't what it was when we started. It isn't what we hoped it would be." He paused. "I wonder," he added, "if anything ever is."

Another Digger told Ned: "You know all the news people have picked up on what's happening here as the Summer of Love, but you know I think it's becoming the Summer of Rape. That's a terrible scene."

Ned said the Digger paused, and then with a weary face and voice added, "It's every bit as bad as the squares out there say it is."

"That guy looked right at me," Ned said, "and he said, 'people don't know what's really going on here. When you go home, don't come back.'"

Ned paused, then smiled grimly.

"You know what the locals call Berkeley? 'Berserkly'"

I looked disbelievingly at Ned.

"But I saw TV stories showing people dancing around that area, what was it you said it was, the Panhandle? And people really did have flowers in their hair, and they're singing and laughing.

"And, you know, all those songs, like 'San Francisco' and 'San Franciscan Nights.'" These were the first songs that came to mind. "Is all of this just a pack of lies?"

Ned thought for a few seconds. "No, I saw people dancing there, too. I think all of that is real. Or maybe it was real at the time the news people were there, at the time those songs were written.

"I don't know what's true about what's happening there."

***

"Ned, do you still live in Boston?" I ask.

"Uh, Marblehead," he replies. "I own a B&B in the area."

"Really," I say. "I'd be willing to bet you're involved, or perhaps you were when we were younger, in your community, too."

Ned studies me. "Well, yeah, some," he says. "I'm on a regional economic board and I do a few other things in the area. You?"

I know that Ned started a food bank. I know he started a program of micro loans to people to start businesses and it was successful enough to be exported to other parts of New England.

I know he bought and expanded several small manufacturing companies in Massachusetts that he overhauled and which provide jobs in places hit hard by plant closings. He insists these be profitable but he is not worried about profits.

I know he made millions running a hedge fund and uses his wealth to serve other people. I know he must have learned a lot in the shock of Haight Ashbury: provide for those who have been knocked down, then help them get up and get going again.

I know all this—and more—because now and then when curious I will research old friends, former classmates and others. Usually this is after I complete research on issues, candidates, stocks, charities and more. The thought pops into my head—hey whatever happened to … ?—and I slake the curiosity. Even if I haven't seen them in decades.

"I pay attention." Funny how that John Travolta line from "Michael" often pops uninvited into my head … it makes me smile to myself every time.

Ned has become what the Diggers could not—successful in helping people, in making the world a better place to be.

"Me? Well, I don't have the ambition you have," I say. "I wouldn't run a bed and breakfast. Too much work. Now and then I will take on projects that come my way. But I don't go looking for them either."

Second, Ned went to Washington to participate in the MOBE or "mobilization" march on the Pentagon on Saturday, October 21, 1967, exactly when Brenda Moore and I were dancing at homecoming.

Ned said there were thousands of protesters who had massed at the Lincoln Memorial, although a smaller number followed in the march across the Arlington Memorial Bridge toward the Pentagon.

"You know, it was fun at the Lincoln Memorial. And I think it might have made a difference in how people look at the war if everyone had only stopped there. Maybe it made a difference anyway.

"The TVs captured everything at the Lincoln Memorial. We chanted 'Hey hey, LBJ, how many kids did you kill today?' and 'Hell no, we won't go.' TV cameras made sure to get shots of girls putting flowers in the barrels of soldiers' rifles.

"Even the march across the bridge went well. Look at the pictures and films of how many people walked across the bridge— it shows how much opposition is growing to LBJ and the war.

"Then it got crazy. Abbie Hoffman tried to levitate the Pentagon to make it disappear. I'm not making this up. People kept shouting 'out demons out … out demons out …' Then it got worse. People tried to get into the Pentagon.

"I think that's when the arrests started, it had to be hundreds of people. But not me, at least this time. I had to run from police. A lot of people got clubbed. Even the girls. I don't understand that.

"It's going to be hard for people on the fence to take the antiwar message seriously when you pull stunts like that one," he told me that fall. "You look at how the news folks covered the march and it's clear when they say things like 'protest turned to resistance' that they're still on the side of the power structure in this country."

***

"Sam Adams, please." Ned gets a beer and takes a long drink.

"My wife and I were up in New England a year or two ago."

"Really? Where?"

"We flew into Logan, rented a car and drove up and down the coast for two weeks. We stopped in Gloucester, Boothbay, Bar Harbor, Newport, Provincetown, Edgartown, Plymouth ..."

"You should have come to Marblehead!"

"There were several places of interest but we just went through or around them, and Marblehead was one, so was Salem.

"We had lobster or lobster or clam rolls, or all three, every day," I said. "It's sort of like drinking Guinness in Ireland: it's much better there. The seafood was much better along the coast than here."

Third, Ned was in Chicago during the 1968 Democratic Convention. He flew in with his dad the weekend before the convention, staying at a downtown hotel close to the convention hall.

"I'm glad I had a place to stay," he said later. "People who didn't have a place to stay tried to sleep in Grant Park or Lincoln Park, but they didn't have permits and the cops chased 'em out."

Ned moved among the crowds of protesters and discovered that this time there was a stated objective: to demonstrate that the country had become a police state. In fact, there was a discrete strategy to use the news media to focus attention on the rising protests against the war.

"You know, the 'Yippies' were brilliant," he told me after he was back in town and school had started.

"They spread the word they were going to put LSD into Chicago's water supply. Then they said that they had a team of women who would seduce the delegates. I don't think any of this was true or ever intended to happen. But it got the media to pay attention.

"When the media found out that there was barbed wire around the convention hall and the wire could be electrified, stories started to question Mayor Daley and the Democrats and how they handled the protests.

"Then when the media were attacked by the cops, even Dan Rather for example, coverage turned on the police. The police were insane, Nick. They beat people for no reason. They went berserk, literally berserk. They even invaded hotels. I heard one cop yell, 'You think this is a kids' game. This is no game, kid.'

"We were yelling 'sig heil, sig heil,' but once even the reporters there were attacked, we started yelling 'the whole world is watching, the whole world is watching.' It still didn't stop the cops.

"But you know what? The whole world *was* watching Chicago. The whole world *was* watching America.

"But what's really important here is that maybe for the first time, America was watching AMERICA. Did they like what they saw? They couldn't. That's the point. Now maybe there'll be change!"

***

"Tell me about Marblehead, Ned. Tell me what else we should see next time we visit New England. We didn't visit New Hampshire other than to drive through it to Maine, or Vermont. And tell me which craft brews we should look for up there, too."

Ned laughs. "Well," he holds up his Sam Adams™, "I still like this one. But there are some fantastic new ones like Allagash and Alchemy and more. You've got to see the White Mountains."

When I saw Ned over winter break in 1969-70, we talked about the first Moratorium to end the war in Vietnam in October and the second in November. These were national events localized on campuses across the nation. I observed the first Moratorium at Kent State, where I was a freshman, on Wednesday, October 15. I did not participate. Ned was among the 100,000 who protested at Boston Commons.

The second Moratorium was on Saturday, November 15. As a commuter student, I was not around to watch any events on campus. There were 500,000 protesters in Washington. Nixon said he paid no attention, said he watched college football that day. Ned made it to Washington to participate in the protest.

But when we met in June 1970, it was me doing all the talking. About May 4. About Kent State. About what I saw that day.

"Ohio" by Crosby, Stills, Nash & Young pops into my head as I recall

that long-ago spring and summer while talking with Ned.

People used to see the "Kent State" sticker on the back window of my car and ask me if I was "there." Yeah ... I was "there."

"I was a commuter student, Ned. I was on campus all week, but only now and then on the weekends. I was there Friday, May 1, after Nixon had announced the invasion of Cambodia the night before. You could get the sense that something was coming.

"So like everybody else, I watched TV or read the papers about what happened Saturday and Sunday, you know, students burning the ROTC building, students protesting or even rioting maybe downtown, the arrival of the National Guard.

"Monday morning, I walked onto an occupied campus. The Guard had bivouacked on the old football field by the gym. I walked by it on the way to my first class and could see soldiers and their tents.

"People talked all morning about what happened Saturday and Sunday, about running from the police, chopping up fire hoses when the firemen tried to put out the ROTC fire, hiding from the Guard after curfew Sunday night. Remember what that cop said in Chicago, about kids playing games? That's what it seemed like.

"People were laughing, giggling, about what had happened over the weekend. People were giddy, Ned. Giddy. Kids were talking about phone calls from their parents to make sure they were alright. One girl said her parents called from vacation in Greece.

"Just before noon, when a rally was supposed to start on the commons, I met up with a friend of mine at the student union. He and I were both going to class instead of the rally. That's what most of the students did, in fact.

"He had with him another student I didn't know, who was excited about the rally. That was the atmosphere, a lot of excitement. I don't think anyone ever thought anything bad could happen. Eventually the Guard would leave and we'd get on with classes.

"I was in Spanish class, taking a test in the Education Building, not far from the commons. About 12:30 or so, we started hearing sirens in the distance and they got closer and closer to us.

"After class, I walked out to find out what was happening. It was bedlam. I heard a lot of different stories when I saw people I knew, but most of them were in unison: the Guard had fired at students and at least one person was dead.

"I had to walk around the Guard by the burned out ROTC building and I could see out on the commons, with the Guard in a skirmish line facing what looked to be thousands of students on the commons and on Blanket Hill behind it.

"I kept going until I was in the parking lot by Johnson Hall, right at the base of the commons, from which I could see up Blanket Hill to the pagoda—which I learned later was where the Guard wheeled and fired at students—and down on the commons over to the tennis courts where the skirmish line ended.

"There were staties at the end of the skirmish line. While students were screaming at the soldiers all across the commons, no one messed with the staties, Ned. Their billy clubs were ready.

"People were screaming at the soldiers, swearing at them, giving them the finger. There were others, who were a lot calmer, who just said things like 'they're killing us now … the revolution has begun, people' … I don't think I'll ever forget that panorama, or any other part of what I saw that day.

"I ran into the friend I had met over lunch at the student union. Lonny Kirkland was his name. He was from Akron. Firestone grad. We stood together in the parking lot for a long time.

"It seemed like hours but couldn't have been. I said, 'Think we'll make the cover of *Newsweek?*' It's not that I was joking. We didn't know all that happened. 'Nah, not colorful enough,' he said.

"Just then another squad of soldiers came over the top of Blanket Hill in our direction, and people started to panic and run. Lonny and I stood our ground for a few seconds and then I said, 'Let's walk slow, I don't want to get shot.'

"We got separated in all the confusion. I stayed for a while and watched, but the scene didn't change while I was there. Students screaming at the soldiers, professors pleading with students to stay back, officers yelling through bullhorns and more.

"There didn't seem to be anything new on what had happened, except word began to spread that the campus was closed and everyone was going to have to leave.

"I had to get to a bus that goes to the commuter lot, which is the new football stadium several miles east of town. I tried to burn what I was seeing into my memory and I have a photo in my mind that will never fade. And then I headed to the nearest bus stop.

"I had to walk past another skirmish line that ran to the south of the commons and along the sidewalk ran within maybe ten feet of the soldiers. I was not afraid, although if I had known what had happened, I probably would have been.

"Walking by a skirmish line with soldiers looking at me was just as surreal as everything else I saw that day. But then some idiot in front of me started walking straight to one of the soldiers and even after all that had happened, he said, 'Hey man, is that thing really loaded?'

"The soldier aimed the rifle at him—he was directly between me and the soldier—the guy just raised his hands and backpedalled. I just kept walking, thinking … *I don't want to die right here because this guy is an idiot* … but I kept watching the soldier and the rest of the skirmish line until I was past them. Then I found out that the buses weren't running, so I had to hitchhike.

"Once I got to the car, I turned on the radio and began to hear what had happened, that at least two students were dead and many were wounded, that the campus was being closed, that all roads in and out of Kent were already closed.

"But I knew all the back roads that would take me far around the campus and out by the entrance ramp to the interstate.

"Ned, probably like you and Chicago or the Moratorium or other stuff, I will never forget what I saw. It was the most surreal thing I ever saw, but that's because it was so hard to believe it was really happening. I had to keep telling myself it really was happening, so I wouldn't lose my cool and do anything stupid."

I stopped. There was not much more to say.

Ned looked at me but didn't say anything either. We didn't know what would happen next, particularly as hundreds of colleges had closed immediately after the shootings at Kent. Kids were adrift.

Then I said, "If it was ever a game for kids, that time is over now."

"Ohio" by CSN&Y is playing in my head as I look at Ned and think about that long-ago conversation with him ... as it does every time I go back to the campus .Yeah ... soldiers gunning for us? Now I know some of those soldiers who were on campus that day ... most of them, kids, like the students ... in fact, some of them were students ...

The weekend after the shootings at Kent, I had a first date with the girl who would become my wife. When she learned I had been on campus that day, she told me about arguments and fistfights in the office where she worked about what had happened at Kent.

I remember arguments too. "Our own government is shooting us" ... "Yeah, and they should have shot more." People think the country is divided now. But I don't think there is any comparison.

I lost touch with Ned not long after. I knew he participated in more protests in 1971 and 1972. But by the time we graduated college in 1973, the war was over, Nixon was in trouble, and most of us were just trying to find our first job out of college.

Ned is giving me the highlights to see next time my wife and I visit New England, and as a native, his take is better than TripAdvisor.

He stops and asks, "Nick, do you think we made a difference all those years ago?" I know he is talking about our generation.

"Ned, I could say that yes we did make a difference, but it would be the 'colloquial we' because it wasn't me. *You* did. Others did."

"I don't know." He is glum. "I remember the Sixties alright. But when I read about the Sixties, I don't recognize it at all."

"It's all in the past, Ned. All we have is right now, in front of us.

We can still make a difference every day. That's what we can still do."

He nods. The smile returns. "I think maybe you're right ..."

I hate all the psychobabble about being present. Whatever. Giving it a name somehow demeans the simplicity of living every day. You can look at the past. You can look at the future. But all you can really see is today. I mean to see every day clearly.

"One more thing," he adds. "We have a house on Martha's Vineyard. Next time you come our way, you come stay with us."

5. The Guy Most Likely Still Trying to Save the World.

Ned Kennedy is still working to save the world around him.

And, he is nailing it ... more than me with this silly list.

I look at my drink. I know how much I can drink, and how much I cannot. I am not anywhere near there yet. And strategically, I have not finished any drink that I started.

Did we make a difference, our generation, back in the Sixties? It's an intriguing question, the subject of constant argument, but it's the wrong question. The right one is what are we doing now? If you're thinking about whether you made a difference then, you're not thinking about how to make a difference now.

Days of rage? Days of rage now are directed at getting old.

"Do Not Go Gentle Into That Good Night" by Dylan Thomas is like one of the three poems I know that shows its face from time to time in this infallible memory ... like right now.

Yeah, maybe if I did go gentle into any *good night, I wouldn't have to take Ambien ... is that heresy or what?* "Volunteers of America" ... just as suddenly, Jefferson Airplane replaces Dylan Thomas ... one generation got old all right ....

But days of hope should never end.

There is no one else now at the appetizer table or at the bar.

Did I say the ten people you meet at your high school reunion? Well, for the moment, I'm capping it at five.

CHAPTER 10

"Light My Fire"

I knew this would happen. I've already hugged more people than I wanted. I may stiff-arm the next person who gets close to me.

I didn't know *this* would happen. I've already talked with more people than I expected. I didn't think there'd be *that* many interested in catching up with me.

And I don't see any of the many guys around the same age as me in our allotment—there were actually more in the Class of '68 than in '69. There were similar large numbers of other age groups, too.

We were the baby boom, after all. There were a lot of us.

At one time or another, most or all of us around the same age would hang out together at one of our houses, playing pool or ping-pong in winter and baseball or basketball in the summer.

More often than not, we spent our summer days at the nearby swimming hole, a small lake turned into a park by the family that owned all the land. We always got summer passes.

We didn't really hang out together much at school, as we were strewn across a couple of grades. Besides, we had a lot of other friends from other areas in the school district. And once we had access to cars, neighborhood camaraderie mostly disappeared.

Now, we are again disappearing.

Dave Canterbury died of a heart attack. He was grossly overweight the last time I talked to him, at calling hours for his dad.

George Smith, Rob Glatfelter, Paul Hobbs and a few others from the allotment died years ago. Last month, I heard another died.

"Ode to Billie Joe" by Bobbie Gentry comes to mind. Yeah, I got some news too ....

Frankie Mecklenberg died.

Frankie Mecklenberg, who I almost killed at the "party" when I tried to leave him behind while the rest of us hightailed.

Frankie Mecklenberg, who hung out with me doing stupid shit like setting off firecrackers at the local golf course.

Frankie Mecklenberg, who got so wild that I spent more time with Greg Kilkenny and his family so I wouldn't get in trouble.

Frankie Mecklenberg, whose sister I chased for years and might have married after more than two years going together and myriad discussions about marriage.

I heard about his death from Steve Kilkenny, the oldest of the tribe, at a July 4 picnic at the house of one of his siblings a few weeks before this reunion. I was invited as Greg was in town.

Greg was only a couple of months older than me, but that enabled him to start school a year ahead of me. He told me that he did not attend his 50-year reunion. He will never attend a class reunion.

Some scars from childhood adolescence, from bullies, last forever and the damage below the surface never heals.

Steve has this habit, whenever I attend one of the Kilkenny family gatherings, of eventually talking about THAT girl. Usually it begins with, "Guess who I talked with?"

Steve has done this virtually every time I am there, waiting until either his brother or sister are there as well, telling us about THAT girl, THAT friend of ours, THAT erstwhile girlfriend of mine:

... where she lives

... how many kids she has

… where she works

… and what has happened to her parents and siblings

Why, I wonder?

Maybe it is because THAT girl and I—first as individuals, then as a couple, and finally again as individuals—were the first in a long line of friends of the Kilkenny kids to spend so much time at the Kilkenny house.

We were about the same age, so when I switched allegiances from Frankie to Greg in order to not get myself arrested or killed, I spent a lot of time with the Kilkenny family at their house.

So did THAT girl, whose best friends in the allotment were Steve and Deb and who did not want to spend time with her brother. At last, I had proximity to THAT girl. If only I knew what to do with it.

***

"You look lost in thought," Tom says. I hadn't noticed his return. "Thinking about all the stuff we did in high school with all these people and wondering how in the hell we managed to survive?"

"I'm thinking about Easter eggs," I say, "and Expo 67."

Tom looks at me as he upends his beer, then as he contentedly belches. "Of course. How could you not?" he laughs. "Hey," he says, "remember Stavarsky and how he butchered the French language trying to impress that girl at Expo 67?"

Tad Stavarsky had mightily embarrassed himself and almost Tom and me with a mistimed malaprop at Expo 67.

***

But I am thinking of Frankie and the favor he did for me.

I first met him in 1962. He was known as "D." His full name was Franklin Delano Mecklenberg. And as mothers everywhere do, his mom yelled at him with both first and middle names. But she shortened it to "Franklin D!"

I guess it's a little too hard to yell "Franklin Delano!" Besides, it sort of loses the intended effect of parental outrage when you laugh back at your mom.

She must have yelled at him a lot when he was a kid because he was already known as just plain "D" when I met him. He even had a floppy hat with "D" inscribed on it.

He and I were pals for several years. But he began to turn dark. It started small. He would catch cats and put them in mailboxes, a little surprise for the mailman the next day. I went around later and freed the cats. I don't like cats much, but I knew the mailman.

Frankie took one of the family cars for a joy ride with some other guys, drove fast, got chased by police, lost control and ran into a telephone pole. He broke his pelvis. I visited him in the hospital. That was about the time I started spending more time with Greg Kilkenny, who was also a friend but a lot more sane.

I spent a lot of time at the Kilkennys as did Frankie's sister, THAT girl, who was friends with Steve and Deb. Steve was twelve months older than Greg, fifteen months older than THAT girl and me.

As our birthdates were late in the year, THAT girl and I were two grades behind Steve, one behind Greg. Deb was a year younger than THAT girl and me. THAT girl and I hung out there all the time. This had the unintended consequence of me seeing her much more often than when I was at her house with her brother. I also realized that offered opportunity to rehabilitate myself with her.

I spent months trying to prove to THAT girl that I was neither idiotic nor inane. After all, she was all I thought about, every day. Every. Single. Day. Results looked mixed to me until Easter week 1967.

We were in the bus on the way home from school. Frankie and his sister were in the row behind me. She asked him if he would help her color eggs for the holiday.

He smirked. "I'm not coloring any stupid eggs." Then he laughed.

"Who's going to help me color eggs?" she said. I didn't know if this was a rhetorical or a real question. I took it as my chance.

I turned around quickly, before any of the other guys on the bus, all of whom thought she was pretty and all of whom were afraid to ask her out because they might get shot down, and said, "I will."

She smiled. "OK. Come down to our house about 4 o'clock."

It was Maundy Thursday, March 23, 1967. My first breakthrough!

"Happy Together" by The Turtles pops into my head. Yeah ... happy together, just coloring eggs. So now what do I do?

I got off the bus, went home and spent the next hour mapping out a strategy: that is, I decided not to say anything stupid, then I put on half a bottle of Yardley aftershave and headed out.

She had already boiled and cooled the eggs, and we spent the next 90 minutes coloring and dying several dozen eggs. Purple, pink, yellow, red, blue, green and more. Like being a little kid again.

The brightly colored eggs were destined as a centerpiece at the family dinner after church on Easter, a tradition since she and her four older siblings, were kids.

We laughed. We talked. I was just myself, no one else. And it seemed to be ... enough, just to be me, whoever that was.

She was pleased. I was ecstatic. She smiled. I glowed. I had long ago noticed that when she smiled, the corners of her mouth slightly turned down as if in the beginning of a frown.

My smile was basic, boring. But she smiled at me for smiling too.

I knew if I stayed much longer I was likely to commit some venal or even cardinal sin of love and romance. "I had better get home before my mom gets home from work."

She radiated happiness. Over eggs? I was so terribly confused. "Thank you," she said, smiling now at me. "This was a lot of fun."

***

"Ground control to Major Tom ... Yo, Taylor." Tom is talking again.

I learned in high school how to tune out everything and everybody, from an interview I heard with Ken "The Hawk"

Harrelson after he was traded from the Red Sox to the Indians. Turn on the TV, radio, record player and read a book. It makes you focus.

"What? What, Tom?"

Tom studies me to ascertain my mood.

"Playtime will be over soon. Talk to everybody while you can."

As an introvert, I have a limit on how many people I can meet. If my graduating class was ten people, it would still be too many.

"I'm getting another beer. You want one too?" I nod. He looks at me again, then disappears.

The egg episode was the start of a campaign to convert THAT girl, to MY girl. Never mind that I had never had a girlfriend and that I had absolutely no idea what to do. It was as if in coloring those eggs with me, she had given me a green light. At least I thought so. I might have been colorblind.

"I got you a light beer," Tom says, and hands me a Miller Light. "You look like you're getting a little heavy there in your head."

I laugh in spite of myself. Tom just grins.

"OK. Who else is here we can get to tell us old lies?"

***

For the next six weeks, late March to early May 1967, I played a cool game and never overplayed it with THAT girl. A first, for me.

At first, I was friendly when I saw her, just smiling and saying hello. I began talking with her for a few minutes at a time in school. I never talked to her too long, always being the first to leave.

I volunteered to help Steve Kilkenny when, as editor of the yearbook, he learned that the publisher had lost myriad photos and sections. I wrote fresh copy that he used, to his surprise, without changes, working with THAT girl as she was helping him, too.

"Dedicated to the One I Love" by The Mamas and Papas pops into my head. Yeah ... and this time not out of the blue but for a reason.

One night when we were working on the yearbook, this Mamas and Papas song came on the radio. Steve looked at her, then at me, smiled and said, "This song is for the two of you." She blushed a little, but never rejected the idea.

***

"Hey, look who I found," says Tom. It is Chuck Long, who was our quarterback. He married another classmate, Katie Josephs. He finishes his beer and starts talking to us about old stories.

"Hey," he suddenly says, "remember Steubenville? Maybe we shouldn't have been playing them, but man was that fun."

Our football coach scheduled us against Steubenville, a team that could win state championships. We lost, but not badly.

***

That spring of 1967, I asked our French teacher, Joyce Bradshaw, about Expo 67. I had a reason. Mrs. Bradshaw got excited and told us what she knew about the world fair in Montreal. There was a pause and I said, "We should go." Her eyes shone like bonfires lighting the barricades at the Bastille.

She won approval from the administration for the French Club for a weekend trip by bus to Montreal. But that was just the start.

The trip proved so popular that the principal agreed to open the trip to the entire school. Four full Greyhound buses were used, and we left from the terminal in downtown Akron.

The plan was to leave Friday night, arrive Saturday morning, roam the exposition for up to 15 hours, leave Saturday night and get home Sunday morning. Looking back, that seems like insanity.

But a number of teachers quickly volunteered as chaperones because the school paid for their trip and admission. I learned that by asking one teacher, Helen Withers, a geometry teacher, why in the world she would chaperone four buses full of students.

"Because, young Mr. Taylor," she smiled, "I get to go for free. I couldn't see Expo 67 otherwise, not on a teacher's salary." I filed that away for future reference and used that strategy to take my wife with me on global business trips. I just had to pay for her flights because most other expenses were covered in my travel.

On the way to Montreal, I made it a point to sit with Chad Summers, a friend of Steve Kilkenny, so I knew him a bit. He had just started dating Deb Kilkenny, even though she was three grades behind. Most importantly, Chad had dated THAT girl, if only one time. I was curious to learn about her as a date.

***

"I miss your brother, man," Chuck says to Tom, and is gone.

Tom looks at me.

"I don't think that was his first beer," I say.

***

I asked Chad about what he found intriguing about Deb. He said she was funny, pretty, inquisitive. I said he was a lucky guy. I actually thought he was luckier than Deb. I kept that to myself.

I asked about other girls he had dated, his secrets to getting them to go out with him, explaining that I was trying to learn the game. He said it was as much a matter of courage as anything, but that he tried to learn something about a girl, then tried to meet her at least once, and only then look to ask for a date.

I asked Chad to tell me how he had gone about asking different girls and he readily obliged. It was, after all, a chance for him to tell another guy about his success. Then I asked about THAT girl.

He said he took her out once, kissed her at the end of the date, but that she did not seem interested in him. "The more I thought about it, the more it occurred to me she already liked someone," he said. "But I don't know who he is."

He did not like to discuss failure, so he moved back to Deb, now that he was successful there. But I had learned what I wanted.

As we arrived in Montreal and neared the fair, we could see what was termed "Habitat '67," a series of housing units that looked a lot like the popular asymmetrical apartment units today.

Nobody knew what it was. But I did. As I began to explain that this was projected as the housing of the future—thank you,

Newsweek—others on my bus started asking me more questions.

Our group was scattered across all four buses, but Mike Hawkins had suggested we gather inside the entrance and we would roam at will. But not me. This was where I would break away for good.

I already knew what he would say when we were assembled.

"How about if first we go see the American exhibit," he said. "It's called a geodesic dome or something and it's really cool." It was actually a "sky bubble" designed by R. Buckminster Fuller, which I knew but kept to myself.

Time to go over the wall …

"Actually, there's an exhibit called 'Man the Creator' and it has more than 200 works of art from galleries all over the world," I said. "I'm going there first, because these are masterpieces that I might never get to see otherwise. So I'll see you guys later." *As in, never*, I think to myself. *Is never good for you guys?*

Geodesic dome vs. classical art? That's like Godzilla vs. Bambi.

I figured nobody would pick style over substance. Surprisingly, two defectors went with me, Bill Wolf and Tom Baker.

And we did see the artwork. But, there were sixteen pavilion halls around the theme "Man and His World"—conceived around the optimism of the time, perhaps surprising given what is generally accepted about the era—and this was just part of one of them.

There were 62 national pavilions, with the US and Soviet Union in a face-off, fourteen provincial pavilions, 34 business and other organization pavilions, 200 boutiques, 76 restaurants and even an amusement park, La Ronde, if you got bored.

We sped through some pavilions, notably the Czech pavilion, as it promised a film in which the audience including us participated.

We sashayed through others. We ate well if fast at restaurants. We wandered through the boutiques where I bought a curved dagger, basically a miniature scimitar. I still have it, too. No exhaustive drug or weapon searches at the border in those days.

My wife once accused me of showing her—dragging her is more

like it—"Paris in 6 Hours." But we did see the highlights, in case we never returned. Maybe Expo 67 is where I got the idea.

Somewhere we ran into Tim Torrance, and Bill Wolf paired off with him. By late afternoon, Tom and I headed to La Ronde.

***

"Hey Taylor," Tom says. "Who else do you want to talk to at this reunion? We've talked to most of the guys on the football team. Any crushes you want to show made a mistake not claiming you?"

***

We were wandering around La Ronde, trying to figure out where to start amid amusement rides, when we both noticed two blonde girls looking curiously at us. They were not hiding their interest. We were close enough that I could hear and, after four years of French, catch a few words here and there. And it was a surprise.

"Il est mignon," the one looking at me said to the other, who, looking at Tom replied, "Il est aussi mignon."

Tom and I looked at each other. The girls tittered, thinking we had no idea they were telling each other that we were cute. I whispered to Tom, "They think we are cute."

The last time I had an opportunity like this was in summer 1966. My parents and I spent a day at Cedar Point, an amusement park now internationally known for its fleet of roller coasters.

I had talked my parents into letting me roam by myself—I mean, come on, I was fifteen, almost sixteen, and with my parents?—and was put next to a guy who was about my age on a roller coaster. His name was Don, and he was from Toledo, not far away.

Don and I started wandering together. Then we found two pretty girls about our age. We started following them everywhere, too. Then they stopped and looked back at us. Don and I just looked at each other. It was a pretty clear sign from these girls they were open to talking with us. Even I knew that much about girls.

We didn't know what to do. We hadn't expected them to stop.

"Do you know what we should say to them?" I said.

"No," he said. "Do you?"

"Not really."

Well, shit.

We stood there for a minute, then turned and walked away. We saw those same two girls later—with two other guys. I am not going to make that same chicken-shit mistake now. If I say something stupid, I can live with that mistake.

Well, merde.

"Merci," I said to the girls, "vous été très gentile!"

Their eyes widened, their mouths opened.

"Parlez-vous Francais?" The girl who first whispered, now asks.

"Un peu," I said. "You told your friend that I am cute, she said that my friend is cute, so I said thank you, you are very kind, especially as I am not that cute. And I do not think of my friend that way."

They both laughed so hard they were bent over as they held their stomachs, and then let loose with a flood of French.

Tom and I looked at them. Absolutely no idea.

"You said you spoke French," accused the girl looking at me.

"Oui," I said. "And I told you, 'un peu.' I meant 'un petit peu.'"

And they laughed hard again, but they came close to us.

Tom did not speak French. It was unspoken that I would do most of the talking, which was hard for him, at least until we got them to talk to us in English. As they could not be sure anything they said in French would go over our heads, they obliged.

"Well, you are clearly not from around here, n'est-ce pas?"

It was amazing how these lovelies, these two young Quebecois, could move so effortlessly between French and English.

"C'est vrai," I said. "And I am about 'fini' with Français."

"OK, OK," she laughed. "English it is. So where are you from?"

"We're from Akron," I explained. "We're on a weekend trip here because this is the world's fair and it is close enough to visit. How could we not come here, and see this magnificent display?"

"You're funny," she said. "And yes, I meant it, you're cute too. My name is Michelle, and this is Marie."

Of course … I mean, how French can you be, how beautiful can you be … and still be talking to *us? Quel chance.*

"Enchante," I replied, elbowing Tom into a simultaneous bow. Michelle and Marie curtsied (really), and then giggled.

"You know," Michelle said, "usually when I give guys my name, they say, Michelle like The Beatles song? But you didn't."

"Well," I admitted, "that was probably next."

Michelle and me, and Tom and Marie, walked around La Ronde, hitting a few rides and sitting next to each other. Unfortunately, we had met the girls late, and we had not much time left.

At one point as we strolled through the park after I mentioned we had only an hour left, Michelle said, "You're not like other boys." I looked at her. I wasn't sure what was coming, or what to say. "I mean, you're not trying to impress me. Too many boys, both American and Canadian, try to impress a girl. But then they are not really themselves. I think who I see now, is who you are."

I was still looking at her. "Is that a good thing?"

Yeah … if you don't know what to say, ask a question ….

She smiled, held my arm and pulled me close. "Mais oui." She kissed me lightly on the cheek. "But you had better go now or you may miss your bus home." She touched her head briefly on my shoulder, then giggled and curtsied again. And they were gone.

Tom watched Marie leave with Michelle, then looked at me.

"Nobody is ever going to believe this."

"Probably not," I said. "Let's just keep this to ourselves, OK?"

At the station where we would catch the tram to the parking lot for buses, we ran into Tad Stavarsky, inevitably lost. The three of us got on the right train and headed out.

The only other people in our car were a severe woman in her late forties with a girl about our age and a boy somewhat younger. The woman eyed us with grave suspicions, perhaps because of her daughter. She had every right. Tom and I nodded politely.

But Tad was never one to contain himself. He decided to maximize the little French he had learned to impress this girl.

It turned out he had learned a whole lot less than he thought.

With unwarranted swagger in his bearing and confidence in his tone, Tad looked at the girl and said, "Mangez moi." Which means "eat me."

I could *not* believe he said this. But he did. He really did. The girl smiled. The brother laughed. The mother smacked him.

I thought when she was done with him, that Tad, Tom and I would be next. She just glowered at us. So much for good relations between Canada and the USA.

Tom knew something was amiss and asked me what was wrong. I whispered to him, "Tad was trying to impress that girl but what he said was 'eat me'" Tom almost choked suppressing a laugh. We moved away from Tad. We could not get far enough.

Tad really thought he had complimented the girl and had no idea what he really had said. Until we told him.

French is *such* a romantic language, n'est-ce pas?

"Crushes? Come on Tom, I would have had to talk to a girl for her to know I had a crush on her. You and I both know that was never going to happen."

We laugh. Merde.

Although we were all so tired from the day at Expo 67 that most everyone slept most of the way home, when I awoke on Sunday morning, I was already thinking of next steps with THAT girl.

And my next steps began right away.

I hit the ground running—literally—Monday. I already knew her class schedule, what halls and stairwells she would take to get to her classes, and I ran like hell to see her almost every class. Then I had to sprint to my own classes. But I made myself visible.

I redoubled my presence at the Kilkenny household because I knew she would be there some nights during the week and every day on the weekends. I studied *Newsweek* and broached topics I thought would be of interest, e.g. fashion, music, and more.

I talked of college, although as a sophomore I had a magnificent 2.3 GPA—you have to almost try to be that bad—intimating that there were several schools with fantastic programs for writers. THAT girl smiled brightly—that smile could light the world— every time she saw me. And she talked with me about the subjects that I suggested at the table, often playing cards, with the Kilkennys.

I hijacked every event to put myself in front of her, sometimes, perhaps, in strange and unusual ways. My creativity in finding ways to get in front of her, no matter for how long or in what place, knew no limits. I wanted her to think of nobody but me.

Friday, May 27, the start of the weekend, I made my move.

I knew Frankie was elsewhere, and I knew his sister would be home. I walked to their house, knocked on the door, rehearsing my prepared remarks. She opened the door, invited me inside. I asked if Frankie was there. She said he was at a movie. I said, *oh that's right.* I paused, looking at her, my life on the line.

"Can I ask you something?"

She simply nodded yes, clearly curious.

"Girl You'll Be a Woman Soon" ... Neil Diamond pops into my mind.

Yeah, you'll need a man ... and here I am ....

"Do you like me?"

She knew what I meant.

Not as a guy among many in the neighborhood ....

Not as a guy who hung out at the Kilkenny house too ....

Not as a guy in her high school class ....

Not as anything but a boy asking a girl about love ....

She simply nodded no. No expression on her face. I could not believe it. She had been so nice to me.

"Not even a little?"

She simply nodded no. No expression on her face. Was she

waiting for me to say more? What was it?

My whole strategy had been based on *yes … yes … I love you madly and want to run away with you … a thousand times yes.*

There was no Plan B because none would be needed. What could it possibly be, anyway … *wait, what?*

I smiled desperately, dumbly, and just said, "OK."

Sorry to bother you … sorry to be alive.

This is how Lee lost at Gettysburg. Why didn't I read military history when I was sixteen? You *never* make a frontal assault. You *always* turn the enemy flank. They don't see it coming.

Duh.

You *never* ask a girl if she likes you. You *make* her like you, then make her *realize* it. She won't see it coming. Maybe.

Once outside, standing on the porch, I yelled, "Kiss off!" for pretty much the entire township to hear.

Yeah, Tom, I'm thinking about Easter eggs and Expo 67.

Remembering how quickly I forgot the lessons of both: just be yourself … don't try so hard to impress others … it will be enough or it will not be enough … and either way you are still ahead.

"The Summer of Love" started out for me as "A Nuclear Winter." And I figured I was radioactive pretty much for the rest of my life.

CHAPTER 11

T om returns, grabs me by the arm that I'm not holding a drink with and says, "Come on, Taylor. We got a lot more stories to tell."

We wander to a corner of the room and I already know the first story based on the first few classmates I recognize: Barry Wilson, Petey Lucas, Brian Tarr, Tom Baker, et al.

Un-indicted co-conspirators, to borrow a term from the Watergate scandal, in the Gunpowder Plot. There are other classmates there who were not part of that story. But I know why they are here, why I am here.

We're going back in time on an archeological dig into the life of teenage boys in the late Sixties. Not sure it's really all that interesting, but well, here we go.

We are of course part of the legend and lore of the Class of 1969. There will be a whole lot of other tales told here tonight.

Because even in an era that brought us the Vietnam War, the burning of cities in protest against racism, the assassinations of political figures, a rebellion against convention and more, there were still hijinks and pranks and other, well, unscheduled school activities that seemed like a good idea at the time … a mantra of teenage boys in most any era.

The Gunpowder Plot—which is how the media sensationalized the case—was one of those "it seemed like a good idea at the time" events but it was really just chemistry meeting capitalism.

As juniors in the fall of 1967, we had choices on math and science classes. I took Algebra 2 and did well. But I eschewed Chemistry 1. The chances of doing well in both classes seemed nil to me.

Brian Tarr, son of a prominent attorney, was an absolute scientific genius. That fall, in Chemistry 1, he proved it. Brian deconstructed an M-80 firecracker as a science project to show how easily these could be made and at relatively little cost.

He scored an "A" on his science project. Then he got the idea to manufacture M-80s and sell them through a distribution network that included other students.

"Fire" by The Crazy World of Arthur Brown begins to play. I almost laugh when the song starts up along with this story because, oh yeah, somebody was going to burn, alright.

Technically, an M-80 was an explosive device, not a firecracker. Cherry Bombs were banned in 1966, and the sale of M-80s prohibited. But not their manufacture. As if people (particularly teenage boys) aren't going to use them ….

"Tom, why don't you tell this story," says Brian, who, as with the others, was suspended. Afterward his father moved him to another school district in anger. In fact, this is the first of our reunions he has ever attended. "You tell it better than me."

"Unh-uh," Tom replies. "You start and I'll fill in the blanks. After all, you're the mad scientist who almost blew up the school."

Everybody laughs because that was the story but it wasn't true.

Yeah, fake news, sorry to say, isn't anything new ….

"OK," Brian says, then bubbles his cheeks to blow out a long sigh of air. "As I recall, it really started in the summer of 1967. My family had a house on Hilton Head, and we'd go every summer. I bought some fireworks in South Carolina on the way. Mostly small stuff, but some M-80s and Cherry Bombs.

"The M-80s caught my attention—they just destroyed everything."

"Yeah," Tom interjects. "All of us went through a fireworks phase so we could blow stuff up. But Brian here needed to understand how they worked, and why M-80s blew stuff to smithereens."

Everybody laughs. Firecrackers are a guy thing, especially at about fifteen, which is exactly when, in the summer of 1966, I bought a bag of fireworks from a neighbor, including several M-80s. I blew up a lot of tin cans. I should have stopped there.

Late that summer, Frankie Mecklenberg, Kirk Sands, and I sat in a tree by a tee box on a nearby golf course dropping fireworks into the adjacent woods just as people would hit their tee shots. Unfortunately, one of the golfers complained at the pro shop, which dispatched six rangers in three golf carts to the tee box where they discovered our hideout.

They took us to the pro shop, then called the police. They took us to the police station, then called our parents. They took us home and put us under house arrest for most of the summer.

We landed in juvenile court where a judge admonished us against a life of crime because he could not do much else: records had to be sealed there because we were minors.

I smile thinking about that episode. My mom was so pissed, but all my dad said was, "I never got caught."

"Anyway," Brian says, "I brought some M-80s home so I could take them apart and then see if I could figure out how to make them. Then when school started, I asked Mrs. Tryon, the chemistry teacher, if I could do an analysis of the chemical composition of various fireworks as a project.

"I figured that she didn't have much experience with fireworks—these were pretty much a guy thing—and probably would think I was talking about those harmless little sparklers. She said OK. So I brought the M-80s to class. These were small M-80s, not the quarter sticks, you know, like a roll of quarters.

"When I analyzed the chemicals, I found 70 percent potassium perchlorate and 30 percent aluminum powder. That was in my report, the analysis of the compounds and how this combination created the flash and the detonation.

"What I didn't say in the report was that this combination was not a firework. It had been classified as an explosive.

"But that's what I wanted to know. I figured that I could get the chemicals, the fuses, and the cylinders to make M-80s myself and then sell them to people. And that's exactly what I did.

"It wasn't hard at all. You could get most or all of the materials you needed at a hardware store or garden store, you know, a nursery. I even made some of the materials. The aluminum powder could be created by grinding the foil from sticks of gum or even by melting aluminum beer cans.

"Potassium perchlorate was a little harder, it was basically a salt but it had to be refined I guess, which took several days. But I could still get what I needed from the store."

"Hey Tarr," says Tom, "we don't need to memorize the periodic table, we just want to hear the story."

Everybody laughs, and even Brian grins.

"Listen, Baker," Brian says, still grinning at us, "you wouldn't tell this story your way so I'm telling it my way. Shut up and listen."

Tom holds his arms up, protecting his beer, in surrender. Brian looks at all of us, the grin widening into a smile.

"I made some changes from the M-80 that I used in the project. That had 50 milligrams of flash powder, or .05 grams. I made the M-80s in quarter sticks, but with ten grams of flash powder."

"Holy shit," says Mike Jones. "Dynamite, much?"

"You put everything into a little cardboard, really tough material, tube, add a visco fuse, both easy to find, and seal it all up. I started making them in the sink in chemistry class—"

"Love Potion No. 9" by The Searchers starts in my head. I smile again because it was the mixing them up in the sink thing that made me think

of what happened later ...

"—and I made sure to give instructions to everyone who bought them on how to light the fuse and how far away to stand for the blast. I mean, this was powerful stuff.

"For three months there weren't any problems and nobody caught on, that is until ..." Brian looks at Barry Wilson.

"Yeah, yeah, yeah," Barry says. "I know, I was the one who blew it. Pun intended."

"Well," says Petey Lucas, "I guess actually I was sort of the start of our downfall."

Tom interrupts the blame game. "Actually, if memory serves, the two of you screwed up at just about the same time, just after we went back to school after Christmas break, early in '68."

Early in '68. The story continues but I am thinking about early '68, before the North Koreans captured Captain Lloyd Bucher and his crew on the USS Pueblo. Before the Tet Offensive when the enemy was literally at the gates of the US Embassy in Saigon. Before almost anyone knew the name Eugene McCarthy. Before anyone could know the awfulness of the following year ....

I knew some of the details of this story secondhand but had not paid much attention. By then, I had been dating THAT girl for a couple of months, and nothing else mattered at the time but her.

"Tom, you were in the car with Barry, not me, and you threw the first M-80 out, so why don't you pick it up from here?" Brian asks.

"Well first, let's talk about Petey. If I get any of this wrong, Petey, just correct me," says Tom. Petey nods and looks at his beer, perhaps in some embarrassment given what is about to be explained, then drinks some.

"Petey bought some of those M-80s and took them home. One of his sisters—which sister was it?"

"Sue."

"Sue found one and asked what it was. Petey asked her to give it back, trying to tell her it could be dangerous, but just in so many words that his parents wouldn't find out about the M-80s. But his sister wasn't getting the message, and lit the fuse. Petey grabbed the M-80 from her and ran to the bathroom sink trying to put out the fuse with water, but that doesn't work.

"So you ran, right, Petey?" Petey slowly bobs his head three times. "And it blew up the sink." Head bobs three more times.

"There was water spewing everywhere," Petey explains. "The sink more or less disappeared. I got the water turned off. Then I noticed burns on my hands from the fuse. I hadn't felt a thing. Sue called mom and dad right away. They were pretty pissed. Dad took me to the emergency room to get the burns treated and he made me tell him where I got the M-80s. He was a statie," Petey shrugs. "I didn't have much choice but to tell him because he might have got in trouble if I lied to him."

"And that's where Wilson comes in," says Tom. "Come on, Barry, tell your part of the story too."

"Well, you were there in the car with me," Barry says. "You tell it."

This time Tom concedes. He is, after all, a colorful raconteur.

"So there are four of us in Wilson's car, a brand new T-Bird, first time he's got to drive this car. We're out cruising the drive-in and the mall, when Barry gets the idea to toss an M-80 into George Gosling's yard. Barry was dating Ginny Gosling at the time."

"Who didn't want to date Ginny Gosling?" says Bobby Turley.

Everybody laughs. Ginny Gosling was, as we said of pretty girls with shapely figures, *built tough*.

"They live a block from the mall. Everybody hates Mr. Gosling. He's the principal and he never smiles, he never laughs, he never gives an inch on the rules. So we decide, what the hell, why not?

"So we drive down the street, it's a cul-de-sac, and on the way back, I light up one of the M-80s and throw it into the yard. It blows up a bird bath right in the middle of the yard. Gosling looks out the window just in time to see us drive away. He didn't recognize the car, but called the police.

"So then, after the rest of us go home, Barry goes back to the Gosling house to see Ginny. The cops are there. And Mr. Gosling recognizes the car because Wilson didn't change to another car! BUSted!"

Even after all these years, Barry is embarrassed, mostly by the fact that he didn't think to change cars to go back to see Ginny. "It never even occurred to me that George might be able to identify the car," he admits.

"Then it gets worse," Tom said. "Barry tells the police where he got the M-80s. Just about the time the township cops show up at Brian's house, so does the county sheriff.

"Once Brian tells them the whole story of the M-80s, and that there is a cache in his and other lockers at the high school, the cops take us all to the school to confiscate everything. Then they call reinforcements: the prosecutor.

"Now we've got the cops, the sheriff, the prosecutor, the principal, the superintendent and all of us and all of our parents, assembled in the high school gym.

"Sheriff Doherty is going crazy. He's going to make sure there are charges filed against all of us. He's screaming that there were enough explosives in our lockers to blow the school into the next county. He's just going nuts. He's also running for re-election.

"Brian's dad finally had enough. He called out Doherty.

"I Fought the Law" by The Bobby Fuller Four instantly plays in my head. I wonder if I am smirking because this time the law lost.

"First, all of us were still minors. Second, there was no proof that any of us made these M-80s at the school. Brian covered his tracks pretty well. Third, even if there was proof, it's legal to make them, just not use them, and it couldn't be proved we did. Fourth, there is no evidence at all that any crime had been committed. He tells Doherty he's going to look like an idiot even if this could go to court because he'd lose the case.

"Then Mr. Tarr asks, 'Where's the girl?' There is silence.

"'What girl?' Doherty is baffled.

"'The girl … the Gosling girl.' Gosling turns white at this point realizing his daughter is involved.

"And Mr. Tarr says, 'My understanding is that she was aware of all this, even storing those fireworks in her locker at school.' Doherty is glaring at everyone now. 'Go get the girl.'

"Ginny Gosling arrives in the back of a patrol car. By this time, her dad is playing down the whole thing. The prosecutor says to the sheriff, 'I don't think there's anything here. We should leave this to the school administration.'

"Doherty backs down, but he's not done. Meanwhile, we're all sent home with our parents. In the end, all of us were suspended for the rest of the six-week grading period that had just started.

"Now the newspaper heard about all this from the cops and is trying to nail down the details. They get the sheriff on the phone and he says that as there are minors involved, he can't release any names. Now he's covered.

"Then he gives all the details about the M-80s stored in the lockers and that there was enough explosive power there to 'blow the school into the next county.' That's such a great quote that all the newspapers and TVs pick up the story, Associated Press picks up the story, and then even *The New York Times* picks it up, too.

"And then of course, they label it 'The Gunpowder Plot' just to make it a better story. The only plot was us making money."

Barry sighs. "The worst part was, Ginny broke up with me not long after. I *really* liked her at the time."

Everyone laughs. By now, given the soundtrack of laughter from this corner of the room, the crowd, all guys, has swelled.

"So," I say, "since we're on the topic of things that seemed like a good idea at the time, how about we get Laszlo to tell his *Cool Hand Luke* story. I don't think everybody knows that story."

Laszlo grins. I wonder why. It was embarrassing, after all. But after half a century, there is little difference between fame and infamy.

"*Cool Hand Luke* had just come out," he started. "November '67. Paul Newman was fantastic as the main character. It was the best movie I'd ever seen. It's still one of my favorites, I mean, look at the cast: Paul Newman, George Kennedy, Dennis Hopper, Wayne Rogers, Harry Dean Stanton, Anthony Zerbe, Strother Martin … what a cast! Paul Newman as Cool Hand Luke just keeps fighting the system and he never wins. But he never quits, either."

I listen as the story continues, but now start to think of what was happening in November 1967. After polls showed low support for the war and for LBJ himself, the president convened the so-called "Wise Men"—veteran foreign policy experts—who told him if the war was going as well as he said it was, then all he needed to do was to promote this progress to the people. It did not work.

"Most guys remember the scene with the girl washing a car, you know, where she's only got a safety pin holding up her blouse together. But that's not the scene I remember the most," Laszlo says.

"Then you're the only man in America," says Joe Garrity. "I think we're all *still* rooting for that safety pin to break."

Everyone including Laszlo laughs, then he continues. "So there is this scene where Luke bets the other inmates that he can eat 50 eggs in an hour. And somebody says, 'Nobody can eat 50 eggs in an hour.' Of course there's a bet. And he does it. I got the idea of replicating that scene, but I didn't think I could eat 50 eggs. Prunes are smaller. So I would do it with prunes.

"I brought prunes to school one day, and after the lunchroom was cleared out, set up in a corner. We had all the guys in the group assigned to play the inmates in the scene, Dragline, Loudmouth, Tramp, Gambler, Alibi, Society Red, Rabbit, all of them."

"Man," says Larry Bitner, "you really *did* like that movie."

"Yeah! I took off my shirt like Newman in the movie, laid down and started eating prunes. We played the entire script."

This is one story I knew in full. Laszlo had advertised the stunt and all the group was there. I was in the lunchroom and they cadged me into watching—I only stayed for a few minutes, but long enough to hear one of the guys say, as George Kennedy said of the eggs in the movie, "get mad at dem damn prunes."

" ... and I ate 45 prunes! I just couldn't get them all down. I knew my grandma thought prunes were a better laxative than anything you could buy at the store, but I didn't think anything of it. I learned later that if you want to use prunes that way, all you need to eat is about seven. And I ate seven times that many."

Cool Hand Luke. Strother Martin and one of the most famous lines from cinema about a failure to communicate. So yeah, Laszlo should have listened to his grandmother.

"I didn't make it through the end of the day. I started pooping my guts out in about an hour or so after lunch. I had gas something awful and cleared out history class. My stomach hurt so bad.

"I managed to get home but I was out of school for two days. I had the runs so bad I couldn't get far away from the bathroom. I didn't even put my pants on for the first day, because I'd have had to drop them every time I ran to the bathroom and sat on the toilet. I was afraid with seconds lost I might not have made it."

"Taking off here, boss." I laugh at that line from the movie—it is after all quite appropriate—and not at what he says next.

"Dumbest thing I ever did. There's a reason the movie wasn't called *Cool Hand Mark.*"

"Yeah," smirks Tom, then he holds up his fingers as quotation marks. "You were 'My Ass is on Fire Laszlo.'"

Everybody laughs. Tom looks around.

"OK, how about the Gaucho King?" he says. "Stern, go ahead."

"Gaucho? I've never heard this one," says Mike Malone.

A lot of the other guys intimate they haven't heard the gaucho story either. It's not exactly a story you tell everybody. Bob shakes his head at the memory, but he starts anyway.

"Baker, Taylor, and me get on the Akron expressway," he says.

"This was that used Volkswagen Beetle that Mr. Baker bought for the twins to drive to school and work."

"When was this, Bob? I don't remember it," says Dave Vaughan.

"Summer of '68," I said. "A couple of weeks after school ended."

It was Wednesday, June 26. I don't volunteer that detail.

I listen to the story as it starts to unfold, but once again think of the time. Late June 1968 after Martin Luther King and Robert F. Kennedy are both murdered, making it a terrible year ... and it isn't even half over yet ....

"Anyway," says Bob, "these guys in a big-ass Chevy come flying by and flip us the bird and take off. They're laughing and everything. We can't let that go! So Tom follows that car and catches them, and we're drag racing on a stretch between the west side and downtown. They've got a bigger engine and keep pulling ahead. Tom floors the VW. We're probably doing 80. And I get the idea to pull a gaucho."

I'm not sure anyone knows why it was called "pulling a gaucho." It was mooning someone, that is, of course, sticking your butt out of a car window at another car as a joke.

I wonder if it's still called mooning. I wonder if it is still done, whatever it is called. Good God, I hope my grandsons don't do this.

"Tom finally catches up to them, and they're still laughing and giving us the finger. But when we pull right up alongside them, I did the gaucho out the front passenger window and all of a sudden these guys are laughing and flashing us the peace sign. It was pretty cool. I mean, we got the better of those guys. That is, until I couldn't get my ass out of the window."

By now the guys assembled for story hour are howling. I just hope no one pees their pants. We're getting old, after all.

"So Tom's driving with one hand and trying to pull me back in with the other. Nick's got my other arm and also has hold of my shirt tail tugging as hard as he can. I mean nothing is working. I'm stuck in this damn window and my ass isn't even budging. So Tom finally pulled off to the side of the highway and he and Nick get out, come around to my side and start pushing me.

"Keep in mind my pants are down around my ankles inside the car and I'm bent in the window like a pretzel, so it's a little hard to push me without pushing bare skin."

"Not a chance," Tom says.

"So these guys take off their shirts, put them on my ass, and *then* keep pushing as hard as they can."

"Meanwhile," Tom adds, "there's a cop car on the other side of the highway and looks like they think we're broken down. They get off at the next exit, and we know they're coming back."

"Yeah, now I'm really starting to sweat," Bob says. "I mean I'm *really* starting to sweat. I'm scared shitless."

Now the laughter turns to outright guffaws.

"Well," says Bob, a shit-eating grin on his face, "you know what I mean. But what're the cops going to say? Are they going to arrest me, or all of us, for sticking my ass out the window? How am I going to explain this to my old man? We see the cop car coming up the entrance ramp about a mile back. We're all sweating now. But in my case, it's what did the trick. My ass and the rest of me was so sweaty, the boys pushed again with a count to three and I fell back in the car.

"I pulled my pants up and then got back out of the car. These guys get their shirts back on so we can make it look normal. The cops pull up behind us and get out of their car. They walk up to us and before they could ask what's going on, Nick says, 'Evening officers, thanks for stopping. The car stalled while we were driving so we coasted off to the side. We thought we better let it cool off and then try again. We were just about to try it when you came by. Tom, give it a try now.'

"Tom gets back in the car and of course it starts right up. So he gets out and all three of us are thanking the officers for stopping and telling them we should be OK to get home. And they just look at each other, then back at us. They've made some kind of decision. Finally one cop says to us, 'You boys have a nice evening. And keep your asses in your car from now on.'"

Heads are turning all over the room as classmates and spouses wonder what can possibly be so funny to these old men.

"And then—" Bob pauses to catch his breath, "—and then, when these guys are back in their car and can't hear us, Taylor says, 'You bet your ass we will, sir.'"

"Wait," says Ken Myers, looking at me amid another outbreak of laughter, "*you* said that?" Not everyone knows my infinite ability as a smart ass—no pun intended. I smile sweetly at him.

"You bet your ass, I did."

The Hombres are singing "Let It All Hang Out" on the playlist.

Well, isn't that special? "Glory Days" by Bruce Springsteen pops into my head. Yeah, but I can't see that we're recapturing anything. Is sticking your ass out the window of your car the glory days? Pretty sure it is, but only when you're seventeen.

Are any of these stories at all funny? Or even all that interesting? Not to anyone but us. And that's because these are stories that we lived with these people around us when we were young.

We were so young once.

Suddenly, it seems, we have become old. And yes … I think I have to pee.

Chapter 12

"Getting Better"

Moshe Dayan is looking at me with his one good eye.

I remember how we all thought Dayan was so cool, with that black patch over one eye. We all knew so little about war.

All the guys wanted to know how he lost an eye. I knew.

A bullet hit a gun scope as he was peering through it in Syria with the British against the French in World War II.

I study the cover of the June 12, 1967 issue of *Newsweek*. It is a color photo of Israeli Defence Minister Moshe Dayan. "Victory in the Desert" is the headline. The Summer of Love, after all, kicked off with The Six-Day War.

"Thanks for bringing all these old magazines," says Jill Light, head of the reunion committee. "They add to all the memorabilia."

I am examining the memorabilia table, which features old sports programs, prom and commencement photos, newspaper clips of assorted games, concerts and play show bills, letter sweaters.

As I look at the letter sweaters, it occurs to me that you could look at all this as mementos of an earlier life—or just its detritus.

"Sure, Jill, Glad to help out. Lots of memories here." It is not meant as an invitation to talk about any memories—rather the opposite because of its ambiguity—but she takes it that way.

"You didn't respond with any update on what you've been doing the last fifty years," she says. "Or your favorite memory of high school. So what is your favorite memory from school?"

"Favorite memory of high school," I repeat. I used to teach CEOs not to repeat any question, particularly a negative one, because it then becomes a quote. Reporters will ask a question a certain way to cadge a repeat for that quote. But who is going to quote me? "I'd have to think about it. And you?"

"So many memories to choose from," she laughs, then scratches her head. "Maybe homecoming senior year. I had a big crush on a guy from another school and he took me to both theirs and ours."

So many memories to choose from. I selected these particular twenty copies of *Newsweek* mostly from the late Sixties as context for the time we were in school, perhaps to help spark memories.

"Homecoming senior year, that is a good memory," I agree. I took THAT girl to homecoming senior year. "Too many memories to pick just one," I add.

My dad kept every single copy of *Newsweek* from the time he subscribed to the time he died. My mom kept every single copy as another reminder of the husband of fifty-five years she had lost. I don't remember my mom ever looking at these magazines after my dad died. Or even at old pictures of her and my dad. She had her own ways of remembering.

Any time one of my two sons—or on occasion my wife or I—would drive Mom to Florida for her winter stay at the mobile home she and my dad bought in the '80s, she had to go the same way they had gone, eat at the same restaurants where they had eaten, stay at the same hotels where they had stayed.

We all remember, and we all mourn, in our own ways.

Now with her gone too, I have all these *Newsweek* magazines. I have seen these hundreds of magazines for so long that I hadn't expected them to spark memories for me. Just for everyone else. But they do.

In June 1967, I went out of my way to avoid THAT girl in that "kiss off" summer. If I went to the Kilkenny house where she and I both hung out and found her there, I rarely stayed long. However long I was there, though, she was icy. Who could blame her?

So I started staying in my room, listening to music. The Summer of Love became for me The Summer of Love Songs. In that early summer, I bifurcated almost every song into these categories: anger at THAT girl because it made me feel better, and mourning because THAT girl was the one I so wanted. If I heard a song that fit, I would sing along in my room. *Ha. In my room. Just like The Beach Boys.*

Everybody else might be singing "Little Bit O'Soul" by The Music Explosion, but I sang the flip-side, "I See the Light."

I saw the light, all right. I told myself that I had been taken for a ride, and I was left with nothing but sorrow.

Everybody else might be singing "Let's Live for Today" by The Grass Roots, but I was singing an earlier hit, "Where Were You When I Needed You."

I thought you were right there with me ... that you needed me too ... but it turns out you weren't there at all.

But then a song would play that reminded me of what I thought I could have had with THAT girl.

I spent much of June 1967 in my room listening to music thinking about THAT girl and going over the lyrics to "Live" by The Merry-Go-Round over and over and over and over. I might not find a philosophy in, say, "Come On Down to My Boat Baby." But, then, "Live," about living, *really* living, until you die, hey, why not? Maybe that means even more now than it did then.

Jill and her husband, who together owned several restaurant franchises, moved to Tennessee to be near their daughter and her family. Grandkids, after all, remain a major attraction. She still handles reunion duties from there.

"So, Jill, you've been in Nashville what, about three years now? How do you like it down there?" It is not meant as an effort to cadge an invitation to visit them in Tennessee, once again rather the opposite because of its ambiguity, but it seems she takes it that way. Or maybe she is just that nice.

"We love Nashville," she replies. "If you're ever down that way, let us know. We can get together for dinner or drinks."

"Thanks, Jill," I counter. "We rarely seem to be in Tennessee, just now and then on the way back from Gulf Shores."

Jill doesn't want to be rude—even if it wouldn't bother me to be alone—so she picks up the July 24, 1967 issue of *Newsweek*.

"Hey, I remember this," she says. The cover story is "Marijuana: The Pot Problem." She looks at me. "I didn't smoke pot in school, I didn't even know anyone who did."

Jill, like me, was an only child.

"Yeah, me either." I decide not to add that I did toke up in college. Once. Really. "Maybe because you and I were only children, we just had no idea what other people were really doing."

We both laugh.

By July 1967, I had a driver's license. I didn't have to stay in my room to flee the world, now I could drive anywhere and, still by myself, flee the world. So I did.

I mostly drove to the mall and walked around because I could. But I still looked at the world through the prism of songs, those that justified what I considered my righteous anger, but more so those that reaffirmed THAT girl as the only one that I wanted.

I sang along with the radio to the lyrics of such songs as:

"To Love Somebody" by The Bee Gees. Nobody, I think as I sing, knows what it's really like to love somebody who clearly doesn't love you.

"Tracks of My Tears" by Johnny Rivers. *Are* there tracks of my tears? Ha, no. They flow way too wide on my face to leave tracks. More like four-lane highways. I drove down back roads, on a shortcut learned from my dad, one day that summer singing THAT song at the top of my lungs.

It somehow made me feel a little better.

But even with my new philosophy of life—courtesy of Emitt Rhodes and The Merry-Go-Round—to live until I pass away, turns out I still wasted a lot of days.

I should have got out of my room or out of the car and gone to the basement to lift weights before football practice started.

The football coach expected us to lift weights all that summer. He even gave all of us little slips of paper with M-T-W-TH-F-SA-SU written so that we could check off the days we worked out.

Maybe it was the passive-aggressive nature I had developed to survive being an only child, but for whatever reason, I checked off two or three days—always different days—each week and mailed the slips to the coach. I never lifted a finger much less a weight.

When two-a-day practices commenced in August, I was battling, as a junior, for a starting position as an interior lineman. In the first few weeks of practice, I lined up with the first team until the day I couldn't block Randy White, a projected starter at defensive tackle.

Randy was maybe six feet tall and about 165 pounds. Not real big for a defensive tackle. An inch taller than me, although 30 pounds lighter. But he was pure muscle and lightning fast. Apparently *he* lifted weights all summer.

He blew through my block on a play over my position and tackled the running back. Coach ran the play again, with the same result. Then the coach just had Randy and me in a one-on-one, and now Randy knew the count. He was by me almost before I came out of my stance. That was the last day I lined up with first team.

I was embarrassed. I was humiliated. And I knew it was my fault.

When Randy sent in those slips of paper confirming that he had worked out, he was telling the truth. Me, I just lied.

Randy, a senior, was named all-conference first team.

It finally occurred to me that I was responsible—no one else — for my own success, and my own failure. I determined to work hard, to actually try, and that included schoolwork, where I had done as little as possible. And that was a lesson I never forgot. In fact, the next summer, and even before, I lifted weights every day.

Jill is getting into using the *Newsweek* magazines to remember what it was like when we were in school in the Sixties. "Hey Nick, look at this one," she flashes the September 25, 1967 issue. "The cover story is 'The School Crisis.' How often have we seen that story over the years?"

"Dozens and dozens and dozens...." I can't finish because we're both laughing, but then we both stop because we simultaneously realize that the school crisis of today is staying alive in school.

"All kidding aside," I say, "I worry about my grandkids being safe."

There were big problems then, but worse problems today. That doesn't make me think the Sixties were some golden era. It was not. But the problems of today: drugs, guns, are intractable.

Or maybe it's the politicians who are intractable.

I didn't like LBJ, but he did pass civil and voting rights acts, Medicare and Medicaid and more. I didn't like Nixon either, but he did create the Environmental Protection Agency, and more.

Now all that the politicians do—those I like and those I don't—is fight.

"Me too," Jill says. "We used to pray that our friends would come home safe when they went to Vietnam. Now we pray that our grandkids will come home safe when they go to school."

How in the hell did we get here?

"Hey Jill," It is Al Nessen of the reunion committee. "The caterer has some questions. Can you come over here?"

I look again at the date of the magazine, September 25, 1967. By this time, late summer and early fall in 1967, I had begun to trifurcate songs, still a few about anger.

"Come Back When You Grow Up" by Bobby Vee. I sang that one in anger too. Until I realized that it was *me* who needed to grow up. I began to forego the fiction I should be angry at THAT girl.

But still there were more than a few about lamentation.

"Hey Baby" by The Buckinghams. I *loved* that song and every other Buckinghams song in a year where that group ruled, if only for a year, anyway.

The only problem was there was no song that made THAT girl fall in love with me.

So now I sang those songs that were mostly about moving on and finding love elsewhere.

"I (Wanna) Testify" by The Parliaments. That was *way* before George Clinton turned this R&B group into Parliament and then Funkadelic.

I wanted to testify alright ... I was still looking up at my feet.

And the one song that really took me from despair about THAT girl to hope about SOME girl: "(Your Love Keeps Lifting Me) Higher and Higher" by Jackie Wilson.

Yeah ... it wasn't that I could sing that song about any girl with me at the time. THAT girl was not *with me. But I could sing that song about a girl that someday* would *be with me.*

I *still* love that song.

One day a few years ago, I took my granddaughter to see my mom in the memory unit of the assisted-living facility where she lived after we couldn't take care of her in our house any more. My granddaughter commandeered the radio and kept looking for songs she wanted to hear, just like generations before her, listening and then dialing again.

And then she said to me, "You know, Pop, in all my years of listening to music, I have found that almost all songs are about boys and girls in love."

"Yes," I smiled, "I think you're right."

She was eight years old.

Love songs helped me make it through the long night that was the summer of love. I would never again so live in the lyrics of songs. I wouldn't need the help for my soul from any soulful songs.

In fact, the song that was of the most help to me that summer was "Getting Better" from the Sgt. Pepper album. I bought that album—like every other kid in the country—but mostly played that song.

"Still going back in time?"

Jill is back. I smile. I was looking at the March 21, 1966 issue of *Newsweek*, headlined "The Teen Agers"

Little known fact, I think, as I put the magazine down, it is Jan Smithers on the back of the motorcycle in that cover photo. Hollywood called after that story ran, and Jan Smithers became an actor. Think Bailey Quarters on *WKRP in Cincinnati*.

I remember every single thing. Useful, useless, or otherwise. A photographic memory can be useful, but not when it snaps pictures of stuff you can never use.

"You know," I reply, "we all can relate the sights and sounds and smells of everyday life to our memories, whether we resurrect them or they come unbidden out of the grave."

Jill raises her eyebrows. I guess people don't talk like that.

"I don't mean to get all heavy or anything, but it's true," I followed. "How many times have you remembered something that happened in your life because of a sight or a sound or a smell?"

"A lot, I guess."

"Can you name one?"

She is silent for a moment, still looking at me. "Yes, I can. Probably a lot. But the first one that comes to mind is the smell of a double-decker cheeseburger. Reminds me of cruising the drive-in and of the boy I dated and eventually married."

"Yeah, me too. Remember when JFK was assassinated? We were probably all glued to the television all that weekend. But on Saturday, the weather dramatically changed in Washington as a cold front came through the city.

"There was a moment in the coverage that morning where there was no announcer talking, there was just footage of downtown

Washington with the flags flying at half mast. But the wind was so strong that the flags flew straight out, flapping loudly in the wind. Any time I hear flags flapping, with the ropes and metal eyelets banging against the pole, I think of that weekend."

"I guess the smell of a cheeseburger is pretty lame compared to that memory!"

We both laugh, but I add, "Well, you know, I like a good double-decker burger, too." And we laugh harder.

"But," she continues, "now that you mention it, any time I hear a train whistle, it reminds me of the Bobby Kennedy funeral train that ran across the nation from LA to New York for his funeral."

"Exactly," I say. "But for me, maybe you too and other people as well, a lot of memories come attached to dates and dates come attached to events. That takes me back more than anything else."

And of course a date pops immediately to mind, Sunday, October 22, 1967.

***

That night, after my triumphal date with Bren Moore, I was at the Kilkennys, talking with Steve, Greg, and Debbie. So was THAT girl, who had had the odd expression on her face at the homecoming dance the night before when she saw me with Bren.

Most people think I am quiet, because often I don't say much. The truth is that I don't always know when to keep my mouth shut. "I had so much fun last night," I said over and over and over. It was, after all, my first ever date, and not only had I not screwed it up, but it was an exquisite evening.

THAT girl had left earlier than usual. I just kept proclaiming to my friends. Who else would be excited for me other than this family who took me in like a stray? "Yep, I had so much fun last night."

"You keep saying that," Debbie glared at me. "Didn't you see that she went home in tears. She wanted to go to the dance with you!"

I looked at her for a long time.

"Debbie, please don't joke about this. It took me a long time to get over her and move on."

She laughed. "Sometimes boys are idiots," she said. Then she shook her head for emphasis. "Don't you know she really likes you?"

This time I didn't hesitate at all.

"Debbie, you have to help me."

"OK," she smiled.

"You know, we're all wondering if the two of you will ever come to your senses and realize how much you like each other." Then she shook her head. "It's obvious to everyone but you two."

Wow. Dense much? I figured "kiss-off" was the kiss of death, but as I pondered this revelation, I realized there had been clues.

After I asked Patty Christopher to sign my yearbook in the fall of 1967—our school issued yearbooks the following fall so everything that happened in the spring including prom and graduation could be included—the next person I encountered was THAT girl.

I asked her to sign my yearbook. To my surprise, she agreed, handing me hers without a word. Still not talking to me.

I had no idea what she would write. I guessed it would be what people usually said when they did not know what to say or did not know you well enough to make it personal, you know: "To a real tuff guy with a great PA."

Yeah, I could have made a lot of money making a rubber stamp to sell with that script, given how often that line graced yearbooks in the late Sixties.

But to my surprise, here is what she wrote: "I agree with Patty, you are one of the toughest boys in this whole school. You can be really nice when you want to. I suppose you know that I am very fond of you, even if I don't show it all the time. I wish you loads of happiness in the future and hope you will succeed in everything you attempt. Remember me always."

Wow, I thought, what does *that* mean? Aren't you supposed to be fond of dogs, cats and parakeets? I didn't know what, if anything, she was trying to tell me. I never knew.

"I'll let you know next time she's going to be here," Debbie adds. She turns her head to the side. "But you're on your own then."

***

Jill smiles. "I'm not real good with dates. I think you're right about sights and sounds and smells. Songs are in there, too."

I nod. "I think you're right about that."

"So," she says, "you tell me what songs bring back memories."

What songs don't bring back memories? Where to start? "Hmm." I buy time. So many songs, so little time.

"OK. 'You Just Gotta Be One of the Most Beautiful People in the Whole Wide World.' Kenny O'Dell. Fall 1967. Actually, Bobby Vee had a version out at the same time."

Jill scrunches her face. "I think I remember that song. Wait a minute. Do you ever even hear that song now?"

"That would be a no. I don't think anyone remembers it."

She laughs and punches me lightly on the arm. "Then that doesn't count. Come on, Nick, give me a song!"

"OK. 'The Rain, The Park and Everything.' Cowsills. Fall 1967. I had this massive crush on a girl and we had just started dating, and that song was hugely popular at the time."

***

It was a week before Debbie let me know THAT girl would be at the Kilkenny house again the evening of Sunday, October 29. I decided that all I wanted to do was say that I would like to call her sometime to ask her out, and see how she responded.

I had been foolish earlier in point-blank asking her if she liked me. It might be no less foolish to point-blank ask her to go out with me. But I couldn't seem to find an opportunity as all five of us—Greg, Steve, Debbie, THAT girl and me—sat at the table and talked.

I finally gave up and said I had to go. So did THAT girl.

"OK Jill. Give me a song and the memory that goes with it!"

Debbie again came to my rescue. "It's really cold outside," she said to THAT girl. "Maybe Nick can give you a ride home."

THAT girl looked at me. She said nothing. But she didn't nod no.

"I'll take you home," I said to her, "on one condition."

It was Debbie who responded. "One condition! Wonder what it is!"

THAT girl looked at me. She said nothing. But she didn't shake her head no.

"You'll have to find out," I smiled. "It's just a small thing."

THAT girl looked at me. She said nothing. But she nodded ... yes.

It was a two-minute drive to her house. I said nothing on the way. But when I pulled into the driveway and stopped, I said, "I'd like to know if it would be OK if I call you sometime to ask you out."

My life in the balance ... one last try.

"The Last Time" by The Rolling Stones pops into my head now as I remember that moment when I was thinking, wondering, do I really want to put myself through this again? *Yes, yes, I do.*

THAT girl looked at me. She said nothing. But she nodded ... yes.

It occurred to me suddenly that she really hadn't talked to me much—at all?— since I told her to *kiss-off.*

But that didn't matter now.

"Great!" I said. "I'll call you sometime this week."

***

Jill is thinking about her answer. "'Get Together,' that song by The Youngbloods in the summer of '69."

Love one another ... it actually seemed possible back then.

"I remember. Now, why that song?"

Jill smiles at the memory. "I had broken up with my boyfriend, but he called me and asked to get together. I said yes."

"I think we have a winner!"

And we laugh.

***

How long do I wait to call THAT girl?

In any event, whenever I called, I decided to call her after school, not approach her during school. Too many distractions, like her friends ... too much of a chance of her seeing desperation in my eyes, too much chance of fumbling over my words. Too much chance of hearing "no."

And I knew better than to call her Monday night after school. Too soon. Too eager. Too much chance of finally hearing her speak to me after all this time, and also hearing "no."

So, Tuesday night after school, Halloween? Back then, trick or treat was Halloween night, and there were a lot of young kids in our neighborhood. I figured she would be handing out candy.

During school on Wednesday—so far I had successfully avoided her all three days, not because I thought not seeing me could help spark her interest but because I was afraid she would say, *listen I don't want to go out with you*—I decided it had to be that night.

I thought all day about what I wanted to say to her and decided to keep it simple. Just say I would like to ask her out and ask when she might be available. I went over this a thousand times.

I still almost chickened out, telling myself I could wait another day. After all, I had waited years. But I knew that if I were to ask her to go out that weekend, I couldn't wait longer than Wednesday.

I thought I might have to wipe sweaty palms before I picked up the phone, I was that nervous, but my hands were cool and dry. I knew the number because I had so often called her brother.

Her mom answered. I made sure to say who was calling. I wanted THAT girl to know it was me. She would know why I called. When she came on the phone, I said hi, then asked if she had a minute, then asked—changing the script slightly—if she would like to go out with me.

For the first time in months, she spoke. She said yes.

I asked if she was available Saturday. She said yes.

"Great," I said. "I'll pick you up at 7."

We went to see *To Sir, with Love*. Afterward, as we walked back to my car, I decided to take another chance and hold her hand. I timed our strides so that it would be easy to take her hand, and when I did, she squeezed my hand and smiled at me.

We had burgers and fries, and we talked the whole time, about the movie and many other things.

I had never had a conversation like this with her. Usually, I was asking her on the phone if her brother was home or telling her it was her deal when we played cards at the Kilkennys.

When I drove her home, I walked her to the door. The tack taken with Bren Moore two weeks earlier—*I don't kiss on the first date*—seemed to have worked well at least for me, so I reprised it.

THAT girl had dated a lot. She was pretty and while somewhat shy, had had attention from boys much older for a long time. In fact, when she and I were sophomores, a senior, the starting quarterback and the guy voted the best looking in his class, asked me if she was dating anyone. I hated to tell him that I did not think so.

If she was surprised at my approach, she didn't betray it.

Maybe she was pleased or maybe just amused. Anyway, I thanked her, and we said good night.

It was Saturday, November 4, 1967. It was the day I turned 17.

***

"You know, it's too bad we didn't know each other that well in school," Jill says. "You're fun to talk with."

"I remember sitting behind you in American History when we were juniors," I say. "I *might've* talked with you then, Jill, but you were always sending notes back and forth with Kyle Messina and whispering to each other."

"OK, OK," Jill holds up her hands. "That's true."

"Besides," I add, "I think we ran in different circles."

This time she laughs, and I am surprised and curious. "You didn't run in *any* circles, Nick," she punches me lightly on the arm again. "You only ran with that one girl!"

CHapter 13

"Fortunate Son"

Pat Kidd is talking about Vietnam. Sort of.

When I hear Pat a few feet away, I look up from the January 5, 1970 cover of *Newsweek*, a photo of Barbra Streisand. An unremarkable cover given recent events: the draft lottery, as surreal as if it were a game show; The Rolling Stones, Hells Angels and Altamonte; even Tiny Tim marrying Miss Vicky on *The Tonight Show* with Johnny Carson and Ed McMahon.

January 5, 1970 was also the day that Ron Brindisi of our class was killed in Vietnam.

Ron was shot in the face by a sniper while on patrol in Tây Ninh Province, close to the border with Cambodia, on the way to the Củ Chi tunnels.

Give me an F ....

"I-Feel-Like-I'm-Fixin'-to-Die Rag" also known as, "The Fish Cheer" by Country Joe and the Fish plays loudly in my head.

Of course it does. Every time I think of Vietnam.

Give me a ....

I mentioned this song to my two adult sons not long ago—oddly enough during a golf outing when somehow we got on the topic of the war—and was surprised that neither of them knew the song.

Give me a ....

Maybe I shouldn't be surprised that few generations after ours have ever heard this song, probably the most popular anti-war song of the late Sixties because of its extreme anti-jingo lyrics.

Give me a K ....

It's not like "The Fish Cheer" (the name given the song because it actually started with one of those words George Carlin said you just couldn't use on the air) ever gets played on the radio. I doubt there's a Vietnam channel on Sirius. The song is not likely to be on the playlist here tonight. But everyone my age knew the song, and the *real* lyrics to the beginning of the song, spelled out ....

Yeah, hey what do you think *that spells?*

But if nobody remembers "The Fish Cheer" by Country Joe and the Fish, everybody knows "War" by Edwin Starr. Even my boys.

Hmm. How in the world did Edwin Starr go from singing the catchy if nonsensical "Twenty-Five Miles"—that's how far he had to walk to see his girl—to singing "War," which 50 years later is still powerful—in just a year? I guess that's how virulent opposition to the war was becoming as the Sixties turned to the Seventies and the war just went on and on with no apparent end in sight.

Pat is telling a story to occasional laughter. Even now it can be hard to laugh about the war. There wasn't much funny about it.

It is unusual for a veteran to talk with anyone who wasn't there, about anything that happened there. I think that Vietnam vets only talk with each other about the war, at their own reunions.

It was no different for my father and his generation. He would rarely talk about World War II. Most of what I learned about his experiences was listening to him when he met with men who had been in his unit. I learned a lot by just listening. Dad wouldn't talk much about combat, although he saw plenty across France and Germany. But he also drove a Jeep, ferrying officers and occasionally dignitaries, like Marlene Dietrich.

This must be different. Pat doesn't appear to be talking about combat. He is just telling a story. I put the magazine back on the memorabilia table and join the group around Pat. He nods when he sees me, and keeps talking.

"After that, I was posted to Tan Son Nhut Airbase in Saigon."

I joined too late to hear what preceded "after that," but do know from talks with Pat when our sons played baseball together that he was a helicopter pilot and had been wounded, several times.

"This one Saturday night, we weren't doing much, just goofing around. My CWO came in and said, 'Hey Kidd, some nut is up in a Huey and he's getting close to the NFZ. He's probably drunk, but if he goes over the NFZ they'll shoot his ass out of the sky. Crank it up and go get his sorry ass home.'"

"Pat, what is the NFZ?" Rick Madison asks.

"Oh, sorry, it is a 'no-fly zone.' At the time, I was flying a Huey, so I took her up and went looking for this guy. Sure enough, he was whoop-whooping around, doing figure eights, barrel rolls, pulling wheelies—those aren't hard in the air but you usually only use them if you're landing in an emergency—all kinds of stupid shit … you could tell he was drunk. I came up on his right side—"

"His starboard side?" I couldn't see who asked that question.

"That's language more for ships, it's not really used in aviation," replies Pat. "Anyway, I'm radioing this guy while guys in the tower are telling him to get out of the area. I'm telling him he better listen to these guys because if he gets to the NFZ they'll take him down.

"I stayed between him and the NFZ for a few minutes and finally he responds and says, 'Seem to have lost my way home, you got a spare key to get me in the house?' And I laughed and said, 'Sure, just follow me home.'

"I took point and he followed like a good little boy, and I got him to where he could land at Biên Hòa, where he'd started his little joy ride, about 15-20 miles outside of Saigon. Once he was on the ground, I headed back to Tan Son Nhut. Good story, right? This was sometime in 1971, August, maybe. But," Pat grinned at the group of us, "that's not all of it."

I'd heard all of that before, but not whatever followed it.

"Earlier this year, I went to the reunion for the Vietnam Helicopter Pilots Association, out in Kansas City. Great barbecue there! So I've got a beer and I'm walking around and I hear this guy talking and his voice sounds kinda familiar.

"He's telling a group of guys a story about Vietnam. He's saying he got drunk one night and took a Huey up for a joy ride, never thinking about the consequences afterward, much less during, his little bit of fun. He didn't realize he was in deep shit until the tower tried to get him to come down. He didn't know what to do.

"And then he says, 'Then this other Huey comes alongside me and the pilot says to me, 'Hey man, I think your wife wants you to come home.' Funny, huh? But I followed him back to Biên Hòa, got down OK and then got the ass-chewing of all time. But I was alive! Never got his name."

All of us surrounding Pat are starting to laugh because we can pretty much guess what's coming next ... and now I know why he is telling this story, because it has a conclusion after many years.

"This guy is getting lots of laughs from everyone, so I jumped in at that point and said, 'I'm WO Pat Kidd, and if I remember correctly, you then asked me if I had a spare key to let you in the house.' There's about two seconds of silence and then first this guy and then the rest of the guys around him just lost it. I mean they lost it.

"This guy, big guy, got up and gave me a bear hug and said, 'Well then, Warrant Officer Pat Kidd, I'm Lieutenant Glenn Rogers, and you sure as hell saved my ass. Thank you, thank you, thank you!'

Pat takes a long draw on his beer, appreciatively licks his lips, then grins at the rest of us, none of us Vietnam veterans. "True story, I mean, what are the chances of that happening?"

Everybody laughs at this story. But nobody asks for more stories. None of us knows where the line is you do not cross with a vet. Eventually the guys around him start to wander off to chat with other classmates. Soon, it's just Pat and me.

"It's good to see you," Pat says. "Been a long time."

"Are you just here for the reunion?" I ask, "or have you retired and moved back here? I think that was the game plan."

Pat moved to Charlotte in the Nineties when his employer, one of the rubber companies, moved its headquarters south and his job as corporate pilot moved too. I haven't seen him too much since.

"Ah, moving back soon," he says. "Marlene never wanted to move, you know we both have family here, but I had a fantastic job. We just decided that when we retired, we'd come back."

Pat and I both had two sons the same ages, older and younger three years apart. All four boys had played baseball throughout the '80s, so he and I got to know each other. Although we were in the same graduating class in high school, we didn't really know each other that well. With 300 kids in our class, it was impossible to know everyone.

During those games, Pat and I talked about careers, and I learned he was a pilot. I asked if flying was something he wanted to do as a kid. He said no. He volunteered for it after he was drafted.

Country Joe … forever singing in my head about Vietnam. Yeah, those boys in Washington need your help again ….

Pat went through initial training at Primary Helicopter Center at Fort Wolters, Texas, then advanced training at Fort Rucker, Alabama. He was a warrant officer candidate, not an officer. If he had washed out, he would have been sent to an infantry unit, unlike officers who were just assigned elsewhere.

"Knowing that I'd have been sent to Vietnam in the infantry," Pat told me once as we watched the boys play, "made me want to pay a *whole* lot more attention in helicopter training."

For some reason, he told me a lot about being a helicopter pilot in Vietnam. For example, unlike much of the military perhaps, when you were a pilot, your experience counted more than your rank. Pat had so much experience that young officers listened to him—in fact, they were told to listen to him.

"It's not like they *had* to listen to me," he explained, "but we'd get shot at every time we went up, didn't matter where we were at in that country, and the new guys figured I knew what to do in most every situation. They didn't want to die."

Country Joe is still singing in my head … Yeah, so pick up your gun … we're gonna have some fun ….

Pat told me while people knew Vietnam as the "Helicopter War," what most people didn't understand was that there wasn't much of a doctrine on how to use helicopters before the war, and that helicopter doctrine evolved from what worked in the field.

Pat told me he flew Hueys for medevac (medical evacuation), troop and supply transport, scout missions, anything and everything. He was shot at every time he was in the air, and most of the time when he landed in the AO (area of operations).

"There were times when we were getting guys out of bad places that I could see the NVA, even see the whites of their eyes so they could see mine too, as we loaded up to get out of there."

Pat said that Hueys had firepower—cannons, rockets, guns—but not a lot of protection for pilots and crews. Some 2,100 pilots were killed, and 2,500 crew members in Vietnam.

Country Joe … I can't make him stop. Yeah, the brass got its chance for glory over yonder ….

"I had what was called a *chicken plate*," he told me. "It was a 22-pound piece of metal you could wear inside your flak jacket, or you could sit on it so as not to get shot from below. It helped, but you were always vulnerable. I was shot down twice."

Standing by ourselves at the reunion, we catch up about kids and grandkids, but there is a topic I want to mention to Pat.

"You know, I read a book that reminded me of you, Pat."

"Me?" He laughs. "OK, I'll bite. What is it?"

"It's called *We Gotta Get Outta This Place*. It's like the Top Ten playlist for Vietnam. It's about all the music that servicemen said helped get them through that place. You used to tell me how often you'd play or hear 'Fortunate Son.' It's on the list."

Pat is looking at me but he is seeing something else. "Yeah," he finally says. "Some of the guys at the reunion told me about the book." He grins. "I still like that song, too. Anything by Creedence is good. But that song was like an anthem."

"Fortunate Son" by Creedence Clearwater Revival was the anthem of just about everyone who went to Vietnam … and a lot of others, too.

John Fogerty now is singing in my head …Yeah … telling us that he is just plain shit out of luck.

"I remember at all those games for the boys—now I watch my grandkids play—you'd talk now and then about the war. You told me that from the air, Vietnam was beautiful, but you were never so happy to see a place in the rearview mirror. I was always surprised you'd talk about it, Pat. Most vets don't, at least with people who weren't there, too.

Country Joe is winning the war over John Fogerty in my head … Yeah, no chance for peace until we blow them all to hell.

"My wife has a classmate that was there—he was a sapper—and he still won't talk about it with even his best friends from school, and he sees them a lot. He goes to reunions of his unit, and no one else is allowed to attend. That's who he talks with.

"I did some reading about what helicopter pilots and crews went through, and obviously it was bad. It's not something I would have ever asked you about. I always appreciated the fact that you'd talk about it, even if just now and then. I figured there was a reason."

Pat starts to unravel the paper label from the beer bottle. He is quiet for a long minute. But he gets the label in one long ribbon. Not easy, with all the adhesive.

"There was …," he says, rolling up the label, "I didn't … I don't … talk about Vietnam with many people. Except as you say, usually with people who were there, too. Part of it was my boys."

Country Joe is again center stage in my head ...Yeah, none of us is getting out of this shithole alive ....

"I brought my helmet home with me. You know it was against the rules but most COs would let us decorate them. I painted O-H-I-O on the front of mine and Buckeyes on the back. And I had a string from Marlene's bikini on my chin strap. I had the helmet on a bookshelf along with a picture of me and my crew.

"My boys always asked me what it was like to be a pilot, and I'd tell them some little story, but never all the bad details. I probably should have put that helmet and those photos away. But it was hard to do. So the war was on my mind more than I'd have liked. It helped to talk with you about it now and then."

We look at each other. "How about I perform another service for you and get us both another beer?" I say. He laughs and I do too.

I get a couple of fresh beers from the bar for Pat and me and we clink bottles. The rest of the reunion seems far away from us. Like say 10,000 miles and 10,000 days away ....

It seems odd a classmate I didn't know well in school is the only Vietnam vet I know who'd talk about the war. Maybe that's why.

"All right," Pat says. "I've got a question for you. If you don't want to talk about it, it's OK, I'll understand."

I try to figure out what he wants to ask. I wasn't in Vietnam. I had a draft number of 266 and a student deferment that lasted as long as the war, 1973. Other friends, like Greg Kilkenny who didn't go to college, got numbers like 88. It didn't seem fair.

"Oh-kay," I draw it out as two long syllables. "Go ahead."

"We never talked about this during those baseball games. If we talked about Vietnam, it was me talking about being a pilot. You weren't in Vietnam. But I know how the war touched you."

I know now where he is headed, but I wait for his question.

"I heard a rumor after I came home from Nam. Even when you and I talked at all those baseball games, I never wanted to ask you about it. But forgive me, I've been curious all these years.

"I saw lots of body bags. I saw lots of bodies. I saw lots of bits and pieces of bodies. I saw friends blown up, burned up, shot up. And I know how hard it was to see all that ... it's not something that ever really leaves you. And I'm glad you never had to see all that, Nick ... but ... Did Ron Brindisi's dad really ask you to open the casket to see if it was really Ron in that casket?"

Country Joe is wailing in my head ... I am wailing elsewhere. Yeah, dads, be a patriot and send your son off to war ....

"Yes. He did."

Tom didn't know Pat well at all. Pat was a country kid, from the southern rural area, if not close to me. Tom was a city kid, from the rich suburb. There was more distance than just miles. But Tom was there. Mr. Brindisi asked both of us because we played football with Ron, we were friends with Ron.

Tom is headed to the bar, but I tell him to get whatever he wants and come back to us. "We're talking about Ron Brindisi." Tom looks from me to Pat, then back to me, then nods.

"Tom was there too," I tell Pat while Tom is at the bar. "He needs to be part of this story. Ron joined," I start.

"He *joined?*" Pat is incredulous.

"He joined after graduation in '69. You know, I'm still not sure why."

Tom joins us and adds, "His dad didn't want him to enlist. His dad wanted him to go to college. Ron was disappointed he didn't get any scholarship offers like Jay Harris. Both went to state for the wrestling team. Jay took third, but Ron lost his first match pretty bad."

"We tried to stay in touch with Ron," I said. "We saw him before he shipped out. He wasn't gung-ho or anything. I think he felt that he needed to prove something to himself. He never explained it. But both of us sent him a couple of letters, and he sent a few back too. He wasn't dating anyone at the time, so it might have been just his parents and us staying in touch with him.

"His first letter, I don't know if it shocked him or me more," I said. "Ron said there were several guys on the plane that literally had to be dragged off the plane when they landed in Vietnam."

Pat laughs, a short, grim sound. "Yeah. Not unusual."

"I got his last letter just before New Year's, on my birthday," Tom says. "He talked about the tunnels and that while he'd been in any number of fights, he was glad he wasn't a tunnel rat. Ron was claustrophobic ... sort of weird for a wrestler, I guess."

Pat looks at us. "If you were in the bush, if you were in the tunnels, if you were in the air, hell, it didn't matter where you were, you weren't safe any where in that country."

We're silent for a few moments.

"Ron was shot in the face on a patrol in Tây Ninh," I say. "Just below his right cheekbone. Sniper. Killed him instantly, so they said."

"Tây Ninh ... that's close to Cambodia," Pat says.

"You fly there, too?" I ask. Tom doesn't know Pat, but there was a classmate grapevine through which we knew who was in Nam— apparently the same grapevine through which Pat knows about us and Ron Brindisi—so he knows Pat flew Hueys and Cobras.

"Yeah, some," Pat responds. "Pilots went everywhere. We were sort of like an American Express card. Nobody wanted to leave home without us ... it would have been hard for anyone to *get* home without us ...."

I nod, but don't smile.

"I guess I knew Ron was dead before most people," I said. "His dad worked in the same department as my mom, and she saw the Army guys show up at the office. Not sure why they went to the office instead of the house, but they did. My mom said Mr. Brindisi was crushed ... just devastated ... I saw that too, at the funeral home."

"Taylor told me, so the next day we went to the Brindisi house," Tom says. "They lived right behind us."

"We asked if there was anything we could do," I said. "Ron was our friend, and the Brindisis were the nicest people. Mr. Brindisi could barely keep it together. He never cried in front of us, but you could tell he'd been crying. His lip quivered. I'm not sure what happened to Ron's mom. We didn't see her much. She must have taken it even worse.

"Mr. Brindisi said, 'I'm sorry to ask you boys this, but ... can you check to see that it's really Ron? I can't believe he's gone. But I can't open that casket and look at my boy, either.'"

"I think Tom and I were too shocked to say anything for a minute, but what could we do? We'd offered to help. Mr. Brindisi was in a really bad way. So we just said, 'Mr. Brindisi, if that's what we can do to help you and your family, then yes, we'll do it.'

"He told the funeral director. That guy was pretty understanding. I guess by 1970, this wasn't the first time he'd helped a family that lost someone in Vietnam."

Country Joe is winding up inside my head ... thank God. Yeah, I knew more than a few who came home in a box ....

Tom and I stop for a few moments. This is not a story that we have discussed in years, with each other or anyone else.

"I saw a lot of shit," says Pat, "more probably than you'll ever know. But I never saw this side of the war, from here at home."

"I can still remember every detail of that visit to the funeral home," I resume. "It was one of the hardest things I have ever done in my life. Tom, too. I don't mean just looking when the funeral director opened the casket. It was Ron. The funeral home did a good job given the damage to his face, but his face was swollen. We didn't stay long. It was just ... too hard. But, then—"

"I mean how hard it was to go back and tell Mr. Brindisi that it was Ron," Tom says. "I think he was hoping against hope it wasn't ... maybe we were too." Tom purses his lips but doesn't falter. "Mr. Brindisi had more or less held it together until we told him it was Ron. He just broke down then. I thought he was going to collapse."

"So we hugged him. Hard as that is for Taylor," I pause and a wan smile lets Tom keep it together too. "We hugged him and he held on so tight I didn't think he'd ever let go."

Country Joe is back ... I thought he had left the stage ... shit ... war never ends for those who lost someone.

"Mr. Brindisi kept thanking us," I add, "and talking about what good friends we'd been to his son. That was even harder. We stayed for calling hours, went to the service and then went to the cemetery. We even went to the house afterward where there was a lot of food and a lot of relatives. Italian family. Lots of relatives. I think we were tempted to sneak out, it'd been pretty hard for us too, but we didn't."

Pat looks at us. "You guys should know, you guys need to know, that what you went through with Ron Brindisi is every bit as much the same as what we went through in Vietnam."

There is nothing more to say, nothing more we can say.

Yeah ... half a century on ... I still don't want to talk about it.

Pat raises his beer in a salute of remembrance, perhaps, to all those people whose lives were affected one way or another by Vietnam. That, I think, might be everyone from our generation.

CHAPTER 14

"Wouldn't It Be Nice"

J eff Reynolds is laughing.
    "Nice hat ... who are you again?"
    If there are classmates whom I did not know well in school, at least I recognize them. Those same classmates have absolutely no idea who I am, I look so different.

Tom Baker is even introducing me as, "This is not Nick Taylor!" He is not always fast enough. Cathy Jones, one of the most popular girls in our class, earlier said to me, "Hi Dave," and then sheepishly apologized when she learned my identity.

"It's a bald guy thing," I tell Jeff, who I know is joking. But I like my fedora, which I bought in Savannah, regardless of being bald. Jeff and I didn't run together, but we did play a lot of basketball together. And at least he recognized me when I walked past him tonight.

"You wouldn't understand," I add. He looks like Robert Redford.

We are talking about retirement. As I talk with classmates that I have not seen since we hit retirement age, travel here and abroad is a paramount pursuit, while we still can, one told me.

Travel is a safe topic—more universally interesting than, say, grandkids. The only one interested in your grandkids is you.

Then, too, you can only relive so many old stories and tall tales.

But classmates like to talk about where they've been, and where they're going, because most of us, perhaps me excepted, never traveled much of anywhere as kids in the Fifties and Sixties.

Anyway, travel actually is time travel. We measure the years by our travels. Was Yosemite last year, or the year before?

I haven't heard anyone noticeably bragging about their travels.

I am always careful when people ask me about my travels. I do not want to appear boastful. I can't seem to tell the difference between exuberance and braggadocio.

Nelson "Nelly" Crist, who became an oncologist, talks about winters in Aruba. He lives in Vermont with his wife, Judy, also a classmate. He is excited when he talks about travel. That is not unusual as so few people traveled then, compared to now.

Nelly, who was powerfully built because he worked summers in a concrete business but now is thin, was the last of a long line of boys in his family, and they were, as we said then, dirt poor.

"All the guys were jealous because Nelly was so well built, big chest, big arms, little waist," I tell Judy.

Nelly laughs. "I never lifted weights. It was all the concrete work in summers. I still don't lift weights. I do pushups—but elbows in!"

We laugh.

"Me too," I say. "Too hard on the body otherwise."

Nelly had two outfits for school. He would wear one Monday and Tuesday, the other Wednesday and Thursday, and then after the original outfit was laundered, would wear it again on Friday.

His family lived in a small house, and his bedroom was a small cinder block room in the basement with no windows. I know all this as I used to give him a ride to school Friday nights to make sure he got there in time for the football games.

I have not talked with Nelly since the Ten—which he mentions—and oddly find myself talking with him at length largely about travel, particularly their wintering in Aruba. I am starting to think he works for the Aruba Tourism Board. But I remember he once told me in high school that he had never been out of Summit County. As hard as it might be to believe, that was not unusual. So Nelly vowed to see the world.

Jeff and I now are talking about hiking, both here and abroad.

"There still aren't any guard rails on the road," Jeff is describing Pike's Peak.

"I've driven it a number of times and it's a little weird looking over the side where cars went off the road."

I remember seeing cars strewn like occasional boulders off the side of the mountain as long ago as 1957, the first trip we took to California to see family in San Diego and Los Angeles. Unlike many classmates, I traveled all over when I was young because my family stretched from Virginia to California.

"I like to hike the trail, though," he adds. "It's about 6,000 or 7,000 foot difference from top to bottom, maybe twelve or fourteen miles."

I have never hiked Pike's Peak—hiked a lot of other places from Booth Bay to Coos Bay. My favorite hike is still London. I always thought we would return to Cinque Terra, but to hike and stay in each of the five towns rather than visit each by boat for a few hours. But the area is overrun now with people like us.

Jeff looks muscular and fit. He is accelerating exploration of the country after an engineering career in Albuquerque, and that includes a biannual hike up Pike's Peak.

Jeff was one of eight kids, as was his father. The family owned farms that sold wholesale to local grocery stores. They still do. His wife, Joyce Peters, another classmate, is talking nearby. They got married in 1970 while college freshmen.

I didn't know Joyce well in school, and although I am connected with her via Facebook, haven't spoken with Joyce or Jeff in years except on social media where we keep an intermittent dialogue.

"How did you end up in New Mexico?" I ask.

I am finding that many classmates have migrated from coast to coast. No wonder I never see anyone I know, but then, I do not exactly go looking for anyone, either.

Yeah ... Chrissie Hynde is from Akron, different school but at the same time ... wrote "My City Was Gone" in 1982 apparently after a visit. Akron had become classic flyover territory then ... but not now ... she even opened a restaurant here ... ha.

"After we graduated, I got a job with one of the rubber companies here down at one of their facilities in Texas," Jeff explains. "We really liked the Southwest," Jeff adds. "Then the company told me one day that I was being promoted, and that I was going home to headquarters back here."

He laughs. I smile. I moved away twice for newspaper jobs but did come home.

"After two years away from here, that didn't seem like much of a promotion. It was really nice there. We didn't want to go home. A big engineering firm in Albuquerque was hiring at the time, and I landed there. We've been there ever since."

Before the reunion, I studied our senior yearbook and did the math on how many classmates married high school sweethearts. I knew about many of them, but was surprised when adding it up, that 46 people—twenty-three couples—married their sweethearts. Most of them were also from our class, but there were a few others from the classes immediately before or after ours.

"Chapel of Love" by The Dixie Cups suddenly comes to mind.

And I realize that it was not unusual at all that a high percentage of classmates married from within our class or adjacent classes. Back then, people did not move so much as companies seemed permanent, not like now when security can be evanescent, so you likely knew classmates for years, and possibly for all of your life.

"Wouldn't It Be Nice" by The Beach Boys now tops the charts in my head ....

And I remember that for many couples who were together for years, waiting until graduation to get married was a long time.

People did not always go to college; jobs requiring little or no skill were plentiful and you could get a good-paying job manufacturing right out of high school especially at the rubber companies.

And in high school, you had a readymade pool of possible partners that you might never match again. Was this, I wondered, a conscious or subconscious thing?

What may be unusual is that so many of these classmates are still together. In fact, I am learning that some classmates hooked up with other classmates after failed marriages, and live together. I know this still happens. One of my sons married a girl in the class ahead of his, but I wonder if it is still as commonplace.

I look at Jeff and Joyce, then around the room at the many others who married from within the Class of 1969. And I know THAT girl and I could easily have been among this cohort. I know it was what she wanted. I took it as a given too. For a while ....

CHapter 15

Tom and I finally find a table and sit down. Talk is tiring for an introvert. I need a break. But Tom, of course, seems to be just getting started.

"You mentioned girls that might think I was the one that got away," I say. "How about you, Tom? Think Becky Price will show?"

Tom looks sharply at me. His eyes narrow. "That's a name I haven't heard in a long time," he says.

Tom knows too much about me. I can return the favor. There are times when this keeps him in check—which is good for both of us. Tom and Becky dated in high school and college and then off and on for some time after graduation, until he moved to Utah. I know he stopped dating her, or anyone, after his brother developed familial ALS. Tim broke off his engagement. But Tom, concerned about genetics, broke off all relationships. He still knows a lot of women—Fantasy Fest in Key West is an annual destination as he apparently likes to party—but eschews any involvements.

"All right, Taylor," he retaliates, "if we're dredging up names of old girlfriends we think might be here, you tell me if—"

"Tom," I interrupt, "I haven't seen Marta Mecklenberg since 1973." I pause. "I saw her when Greg Kilkenny got married."

Tom is silent, unusual for him, but not for long. "At least I had a good reason for breaking it off with Becky," he says. "You know that as well as I do. What's your excuse?"

***

"Your mother wants you to do what?"

I look at Marta Mecklenberg.

I still did not know why THAT girl ever looked at me.

Marta was stunning. Why in the world was she with me? I would feel that way later about my wife, too. But Marta, a member of the homecoming court, was pursued by lots of guys who were willing to ask her out, and watched by many more who were too afraid.

She was 5'4" and weighed 110 pounds, an hourglass figure. She had chestnut hair—although surprisingly she had black eyebrows that seemed stitched—and hazel eyes with flecks of gold.

She had an aquiline nose—I once told her even before we started dating that she had a "Roman nose." She thought it was a criticism. I told her it was noble, a nose of the nobility of ancient Rome. She laughed, her little heh-heh laugh, and said all right.

Me? I was just average looking. Brown hair, brown eyes, ears that stuck out a little too much for me—I always envied people with ears seemingly pinned to their heads.

What I heard was that girls considered me "cute." Marta told me that's what her girlfriends said about me. *"Oh, he's cute!"* I took that to mean *you're not exactly handsome, but not exactly ugly either, somewhere in between.*

Yeah and now I'm at the age that when my wife and I hold hands, some young people say, "that's so cute" … I always feel like saying, "Hey, cute this … I got your cute right here …."

Marta and I had been dating for six months by this time, May 1968. It was the month between assassinations in America, as though we had taken a break from killing, the month when protests erupted in Paris and across France, as if the communes had returned.

"My mom wants me to enter the contest for queen of the Cherry

168

Blossom Festival," she said.

The Cherry Blossom Festival occurred every May in Barberton, a largely industrial city southwest of Akron, not far from us. The signal event was the crowning of the Cherry Blossom Queen, and every year dozens of girls competed for the title.

It was quintessential small town. I remember as a Kent freshman in Honors English in fall 1969, hearing a classmate from Circleville, another small town, criticize her hometown for its pumpkin festival. "There's a war going on," she said. "It shows no sign of stopping regardless of what Nixon said before the election. And people want to celebrate pumpkins? We should be stopping the war."

The rest of us, ten or twelve students in all, were silent.

The professor looked at her and said, "What is wrong, young lady, with celebrating pumpkins? It is really celebrating life. We all want the war to end. But it is because there is a war that we should celebrate life, whether a pumpkin festival or otherwise."

Marta studied me, slightly forlorn about the Cherry Blossom thing. "She thinks it will be a good addition to my application for college."

I wasn't sure how to respond. "What do you think?" I finally asked.

"I don't want to do it. I don't think I'm pretty enough."

Some girls might utter such a line to elicit a compliment. She was not one of them. This was what she actually thought.

"You have no idea," I said, "do you?" And only briefly paused.

"I think you should enter the contest. Win or lose, it will be a good experience for you. And it'll be fun. You'll ride in the parade in a convertible and wave at all the people. You'll look great in the swimsuit competition, I already know that. And we'll go to the formal dance at the end of the day."

She was not convinced.

"And I'll get to brag about my beauty queen girlfriend."

Marta laughed.

I was still trying to understand what it meant to have a girlfriend.

I was trying harder to understand what it meant to be a boyfriend. She entered the contest. She did not win. But we had fun.

The parade started at 10 a.m. Downtown streets were closed. She was nervous. I told her I would be there every step of the way, and I was. She sat atop the back seat of a GTO convertible.

When she was introduced at the formal, I waited at the bottom of the steps from the stage to escort her after her introduction. "You look fantastic," I said. And she beamed.

What did it mean to be a boyfriend?

You were there for her, for one thing. Always.

***

"Nick Taylor."

Tom nudges me. But it is not him speaking.

I look at him. He nods up. So I look up.

"Ronnie Reich."

Ronnie had to look at my name tag. I do not have to look at his. No handshakes. No hugs. Just smiles. Ronnie and I were good friends as juniors but mostly went separate ways as seniors. I always hung with the Baker boys and all the Kilkenny kids, even as other friends came and went.

"Are you still in Youngstown?" I ask, last known address.

"No, we live in Kent, about twelve years now," Ronnie says.

Ronnie was big in high school and started ahead of me at tackle, so the coaches moved me to end because none of the ends could block and I could. He is absolutely massive now, 250 pounds at least. I went the other way, losing more than 30 pounds, perhaps one reason so few classmates recognize me now.

"My company closed the office I ran out there and wanted me to run the office in Cleveland. Gail was assistant superintendent in Youngstown. We picked a place that was equidistant."

I remember Gail, who Ronnie met early on in college. She was from Youngstown. As often happens when couples marry, they moved to the hometown of the girl. Gail is a funny and friendly lady.

"Is your wife here?" Gail smiles.

"No, she thinks I'll only talk with her. This is her way of making me be sociable," I say. Gail laughs. I am only telling the truth. "But her mom is in hospice, and my wife and her siblings are there a lot to make sure she gets appropriate care."

Gail looks at me. There is care and concern in her eyes. "What's your mother-in-law's name?"

"Rosemary."

"*Rose*-mary." Gail slowly repeats, then touches my arm. "I will pray for Rosemary."

I believe her.

Ronnie, Gail and I talk a little longer. Inevitably, we discuss travel. I do not know what he remembers. Like double dating, with *all* the girls he dated—and there were a lot of them—usually at drive-ins because it was cheap.

Like Ronnie telling me, "You're pw'd!" when I told him the song "Spazz" by The Elastik Band was insensitive after first saying the lyrics were funny, freely admitting I was disabused of the idea by my new girlfriend, THAT girl.

Like Ronnie and me and our dates, driving in a snowstorm to the annual Sadie Hawkins dance and then to dinner at that Middle Eastern place (where this time I remembered to get a reservation), and where we laughed for hours.

Like Ronnie, his dad, and me in front of a little portable black and white TV on their kitchen table, watching the Packers and Cowboys in what now is known as the legendary "Ice Bowl" game that just happened to be New Year's Eve 1967.

Like inviting Ronnie and Greg to my house that same night, after the party arranged by my parents fell apart when my mom's sisters and their husbands got the flu; the three of us playing cards deep into the night and me driving them home, all of us uproarious, with the windows down so we could see the road because the windshield was iced over.

Like me getting Ronnie a job during freshman year in college, me at Kent and him at Akron, at an upscale restaurant at the mall, where we gabbed all through college about girls, sports, and ….

But there is *one* memory that I *know* Ronnie will not forget.

One day senior year, he and I were walking through the halls on the way to homeroom, and he had on a shirt that had *69* in big—I mean *big*—letters on the front and back. The principal disapproved— it did not matter that ours was in fact the Class of 69— and sent Ronnie home to change his shirt. Ronnie had anticipated this and came back to school with a shirt just like the first one with 68 1/2 both front and back. And then got sent home again, to stay for the day.

"My son got married in Nice, France," Ronnie says. And I note that like many people, Ronnie says "my" instead of "our," even with his wife by his side, to describe their children.

"So we took a river cruise up the Rhone."

"You have to tell me about it," I say. "Never done that before."

"It was so much fun," Gail adds. "Have you taken any cruises?"

I pause.

The most interesting was in the Galapagos, which we visited along with Machu Picchu after I spoke about the future of media and media relations at a global PR conference in Lima, Peru. But will that sound like exuberance or braggadocio?

There are times, even at my age, when I am still self-conscious.

Somehow I had established a reputation as one of the best media relations and crisis management professionals extant, but I let journalists, executives and colleagues say so, not me. I learned how to see around corners and tell clients what would happen next … and next … and what their next steps could be.

"You," said the head of corporate communications for one of the largest companies in the world, "are an unbelievable sage."

I was so flattered, but immediately my infinite memory reminded me of Bill Murray in *Groundhog Day:* " *You're too kind … you're probably right.* "

Just let your client flatter you. Did I really believe what she said? Doesn't matter. At least she thinks it's true. A happy client is good.

"We did an Alaskan cruise," I reply. "My wife ran a beauty salon, and she heard about all kinds of vacations. People told her that most destinations were never as much fun as they thought. But the two that always exceeded expectations," I hurriedly add, "were Hawaii and an Alaskan cruise."

"Tell us all about it because we want to go too!" Gail says.

***

"I forgot to tell my mom where we're going," Marta says.

It is the summer of 1968. *This* is the summer of love for me.

"We can go back and tell your mom we're going on a picnic, or we can find a pay phone and you can call her, if she's home."

Marta is silent. "Well, she saw me making sandwiches ...."

"We'll find a gas station with a pay phone and you can call."

I know that her mom worries about her two younger daughters, Greta and Marta, because the eldest had to get married—not common knowledge—but Marta explained the situation.

I understand when Mrs. Mecklenberg now and then cautions us when she thinks we spend too much time together. "Too much of a good thing" is all she says ... code ....

Picnics, too, are cheap but fun dates. Money is always scarce. We spread a blanket in the sunshine of a wooded space, then turn on the radio and listen.

"This Guy's in Love With You" by Herb Alpert (a great, and I mean *great*, make-out song, by the way).

"The Look of Love" by Sergio Mendes & Brasil 66.

"Mrs. Robinson" by Simon and Garfunkel.

"Pictures of Matchstick Men" by Status Quo.

"Stone Soul Picnic" by The 5th Dimension.

"Hey Jude" by The Beatles.

And on and on and on ....

We eat bologna and cheese sandwiches, potato chips, and her

homemade cookies, and drink whatever flavor soda pop my dad has stocked in our basement. For some reason, my dad kept cartons and cartons of pop—often it was diet soda like Diet Rite or Tab both pretty awful, but he also favored Pepsi. This made me immensely popular as a kid.

And then we spread another blanket in the shade and make out. Until one time ....

"Hey, woo hoo, having fun down there!?"

This time, we had situated ourselves next to a horse trail and a line of couples on horses ambles just yards from us.

"I'm so embarrassed," she says, and we stop, for a bit.

I found it odd that she did not like PDA. Public displays of affection to us Baptists were very much disapproved of by my church, but not so much by hers—she was Catholic. We rarely kissed in public.

I had never kissed a girl until the second date with Marta, and even then I mostly missed her lips in a sideswipe.

"I missed," I sheepishly admitted. Captain Obvious, much?

"Maybe you should try again," she said, and so I did.

Only once do we come close to giving Mrs. Mecklenberg a real reason to worry. It is Wednesday, August 21, 1968, the day after the Russian invasion of Czechoslovakia. Marta and I had bivouacked in a private area on yet another picnic, and it isn't just the weather getting hot as we make out.

"Marta," I say, "we'd better stop."

"I'm glad you stopped," she says. "I don't think I could've ...."

What does it mean to be a boyfriend?

You put her first, before you ... always.

***

"It was a seven-day cruise," I explain to Gail and Ronny. "Uh, it was on Holland America. It was for our fortieth anniversary. We had an outside room and balcony, and sipped champagne or mimosas in the mornings."

"Nice!" Gail is excited.

"We stopped in Ketchikan, Sitka and Juneau. Then in Victoria on Vancouver Island on the way back to Seattle. We had the best dumplings at a little restaurant in Sitka. We took the bus to the helicopter that landed us on a glacier, then tipped the driver well on the return and asked her for restaurant ideas. She told us about this little hole-in-the-wall place that only served dumplings and only two kinds of dumplings: regular and hot. Just plastic plates and cutlery, but the best food the whole trip.

"We took several shore excursions, including the helicopter ride to the glacier, which was more or less like walking around outside your house in the snow. But fun just to say you did it."

Gail is clearly taking mental notes.

"We also went whale watching, and for a long time it looked like we weren't going to see any whales. But there was one, then two and finally half a dozen, and the younger ones put on a show for us, breaching high in the air and then collapsing in the water.

"On the last stop, in Victoria, we did 'high tea' at this magnificent old hotel—the Empress Hotel—and it was elegant but really not at all pretentious. Well worth the time."

"Ronnie, we have to go!"

***

"Mom, we have to go!"

Christmas 1967. I cajoled my mom into helping shop for Marta. I had no idea what to buy for a girl, especially a new girlfriend.

"I know she's a nice girl," Mom said while we were shopping. "But why can't you find a girl in our church?"

Years later, when I started dating a girl from our church who would become my wife, my mom said, "Whatever happened to that nice little Catholic girl?" Apparently there would be no *Good Housekeeping* "seal of approval" for any girl I dated or married.

"Mom," I said, "I like this girl, regardless of what church she attends."

"Wild Honey" by The Beach Boys comes to mind. Yeah ... what good did it do you, mom? You could frown all you wanted and it wouldn't have made a damn bit of difference ....

So I told my mom what Marta seemed to like, and Mom found two outfits that were welcomed. But those outfits did not come close to the gaggle of gifts Marta got for me, shirts, what were then called CPO jackets and more.

***

"Do you have other trips planned?" I ask. I do not want to sound as if I am uninterested in Ronnie and Gail.

"I'd like to go to Germany," Ronnie says.

"With a name like Reich, how could you not?!"

We laugh.

"Ronnie is taking me to Aruba for Valentine's Day," Gail says. "I know it's an act of love because Ronnie doesn't like heat!"

***

"I hope your heater gets going soon," said Ronnie. "It's freezing."

We were headed to the mall for shopping during the Christmas break in December 1967, and just before we disagreed on what, exactly, the lyrics were to "Daydream Believer," Ronnie asked, "Do you love her?"

"What?"

"Do you love her?"

I glanced at him. "Ronnie, we've been dating for six weeks ...."

"Would you marry her?"

I was silent. "After we graduate from high school and then college, and if we are still together ... yes, I, maybe then, I would marry her."

"Then you love her."

***

"That's how I know Ronnie loves me!" Gail is ecstatic. "I didn't even have to beg Ronnie to go to Aruba!"

I am listening to Gail and remembering Ronnie. We were such good friends in the last half of '67, more so first half of '68. And I am thinking, *Ronnie, you really hit the jackpot with this one.*

I remember that last half of '67 but more so the first half of '68. *Just how many girls was it who dumped you, Ronnie?* Seems like Ronnie was always crying on my shoulder.

He was on a losing streak—"Satisfaction" by The Rolling Stones comes to my mind—no girly action for him for a whole year.

I remember every single thing that happened, or at least that was reported, in January and February 1968.

On January 5, the Vietnam War took a surreal twist; when even the famous pediatrician Dr. Benjamin Spock—whose book *Baby and Child Care* was used by at least one generation of mothers and whose book was one of the best sellers of all time— was arrested for alleged conspiracy to encourage draft dodgers.

I saw the fault lines everywhere straining a society.

On January 23, the North Koreans captured the USS Pueblo and incarcerated its crew as criminals for 11 months. A photo of the crew taken by their captors backfired when it was discovered that the crew was using hand signals, including flipping the bird, to show the US what was happening.

I saw the courage of people who never gave up hope.

On January 31, the North Vietnamese attacked American installations across South Vietnam, including the US Embassy in Saigon, contravening the LBJ administration claim that the US was winning the war. The Tet Offensive was a military disaster, but a perception coup as the fact of the attack shook America.

I saw the lies of a government that seemingly never spoke truth.

On February 1, South Vietnamese General Nguyen Ngoc Loan put a gun to the head of a handcuffed Viet Cong and killed him—all captured by photo and film. The VC had just allegedly murdered another South Vietnamese officer and his family.

I saw the viciousness of a war like every other war.

On February 7, Associated Press reporter Peter Arnett, reporting from Vietnam, quoted a US Army major as saying, "We had to destroy the village in order to save it."

I saw the insanity of a war with no apparent purpose.

On February 27, Walter Cronkite told the nation, "It is increasingly clear to this reporter that the only rational way out then will be to negotiate, not as victors, but as an honorable people who lived up their pledge to defend democracy, and did the best they could."

And I saw how this report would change the war ... and media.

For the record, it was five—*five*—girls who dumped Ronnie Reich in the last half of '67 and first half of '68, starting with Patty Christopher. It was almost like a parade in the rain. It was some kind of really weird chain reaction, where girls would go out with him a couple of times and then immediately start going steady with some other guy. I had never seen anything like it.

Ronnie spent a lot of time commiserating with me, me who finally had a girl, THAT girl, and he told me it was all because: "I'm an idiot."

***

"I'm an idiot." Ronnie Reich turns back to me as he and Gail prepared to talk to others. "Almost walked away without trading phone numbers."

"No more than me," I laugh. We trade numbers and pledge to get together, and then we just look at each other and once again smile.

I remember seeing the same smile between my dad and Bob Morrison when my wife and I held a 50th anniversary party for my folks in 1995. My parents married two weeks after he got home from Europe with hundreds of GIs on the Queen Mary.

Bob Morrison and my dad had known each other since they were ten and spent a lot of the Thirties together, even though my dad, as the oldest of seven, dropped out of high school for two years. He drove a massive truck for the hauling business started by his stepfather, which failed. Dad went back to high school and graduated two years late … just in time for the war.

But Bob and my dad had their adventures, including taking a trip to Pittsburgh where they would drive fast then screech to a halt at a light or stop sign, until the brakes gave out. They didn't cause an accident, so the cops said, "Boys, you need to get on home."

It is that sort of smile between Ronnie Reich and me—old friends who have a shared history, even if it was long ago.

I remember when Ronnie started dating Gail. He had more or less sworn off of girls our senior year of high school, but met her in the first quarter of college. Just like all the others, Gail *did* start going steady with a guy after dating Ronnie a couple of times.

It was Ronnie.

CHAPTER 16

"Tom."

    "What?"

    "Stop talking."

"What?"

"Becky Price just walked in the door."

"Then You Can Tell Me Goodbye" by The Casinos starts to play on the reunion playlist.

A million years to make it work out … turns out a million years ain't what it used to be ….

The playlist is utterly appropriate for Tom, and for me, too.

"Tom."

"What?"

"Did you hear me? Becky Price just—"

"I heard you," Tom says.

"Are you going to talk to her?"

"Probably."

"It's not like you, not to know what to say."

"Well, Becky Price is not like anyone else here."

I stroke the chin under my beard for a few seconds. "I understand."

***

I do not understand.

"Tell Me You Love Me" was on the car radio, but Marta wanted me to change the channel. She hated that song.

"Why?"

"I don't want to ever think about breaking up."

This was not the only time she did not want to hear a song about lovers in trouble. In fact, I was to hear this lament about many songs, like, "How'd We Ever Get This Way" by Andy Kim.

Yeah, how did it start ? How would it end? Poignant ....

It was Thursday, May 30, 1968—Memorial Day—when that was still on a specific date instead of a reason for a long weekend. We were headed to a picnic with the Kilkenny family, and Andy Kim, usually upbeat, was singing the blues.

"Please find another song," said Marta. "I hate that song." I looked sidelong at her, then started turning the radio dial.

I stopped on Tommy James and the Shondells singing, "Mony Mony." Tommy James got the idea for that song when he saw the Mutual of New York sign—MONY— when in New York City. It was a great song ... a *great* song ... even if nobody ever knew a girl named Mony.

She smiled. "That's much better." *That's much better.* I heard that more than a few times. At least back then, it was easier to change the station.

There were other words she would say to me, many times.

For example: "You're so smart."

"Not really ...."

"How did you know he wasn't going to run?"

It was Monday, April 1, 1968, three days before Martin Luther King Jr. was shot in Memphis, and one day after Lyndon Johnson announced on national television he was not running again.

On Friday, March 29, it was announced that LBJ would make a televised speech from the White House the coming Sunday evening.

That Friday evening, Marta and I were stashed on a sofa in the basement, sorta watching a movie, and sorta not so much.

When we caught our breath, we watched the news.

"He's not going to run," I said when we heard about the speech.

"What?" Marta was puzzled.

"He's not going to run … Johnson … he's going to say he's not going to run for re-election."

Marta looked at me when the school week started that Monday, curiosity and wonder on her face. "But, how could you possibly know?" she asked.

It wasn't that hard to figure out.

"Look, Johnson was already in trouble because of Tet. People saw on television that whatever else was happening in Vietnam, we were not winning the war. Then he won the New Hampshire primary but not by much over McCarthy. Then Bobby Kennedy announced he's running for president. It's clear Johnson is unpopular. And with Bobby in the race, Johnson must know it would be hard to win the nomination, much less the election."

She looked at me and slowly shook her head a few times.

"You're so smart."

If only, I have thought so many times, that was really true.

***

"Tom, you need to talk with her. It'll seem strange if you don't. You two dated for a long time. Aren't there things you left unsaid at the time that you want to talk about? Or just talk to her to find out how her life has turned out?"

Tom looks at me. His lips are pursed. "OK wise guy, do you know what you would say to Marta?"

"Are you ready to go back to Titanic?" Yeah, so yet another random thought pops into my head. At least it's not a song this time.

"Yes," I smile. "I do. But I wouldn't bet on me actually doing it either."

"Haaaaahaaaahaaahaaahaaa, that's funny Taylor."

I smile.

Tom sits up straight, folds his hands on the table. "I'd like it better if she came over here to talk with me—"

I interrupt. "Yeah, but you're the one who broke up with her."

"—but I'm the one who broke up with her so the chances that she'll come over here are pretty slim. So I'm going to wait here with you for a bit so it doesn't look like I'm rushing over there to see her as soon as I see her walk in the door. After all, I don't know if she'll hug me or slap me."

I nod. Makes sense.

"So," Tom has an evil grin. "What *would* you say to her?"

"I am so sorry."

***

Marta was still angry and so hurt, and I couldn't blame her. I was amazed she was even talking to me, that she hadn't given up on me or said she was breaking up with me.

It was Wednesday, August 28, 1968. Chicago was a war zone as the Democratic National Convention saw anti-war protests that inflamed the city. We were at the Kilkennys playing cards—euchre—with Steve and Greg, a frequent activity.

Steve and Marta were arrayed against Greg and me. We were tied 8-8 and I had named suit—hearts—and we were set. Steve and Marta laughed and Marta teased me about them winning and us losing.

I glowered, darkened, then exploded.

"You can take those goddamn cards and shove them up your ass." The words come out of my mouth before I could stop them, before I even knew I had fired those awful bullets at her.

Greg said, "Wow." Steve was wide-eyed. And Marta had tears in her eyes. Her lip trembled but she wouldn't let herself cry. She was defiant against the meanness that I displayed toward her.

We drove home in silence. I said I was sorry when we arrived at her house but she didn't look at me, didn't acknowledge me in any way. She simply closed, not slammed, the door, and went inside.

Forever, I wondered?

We had been dating, as steadies, almost a year. I had only one date after the first date with Marta. That was a date already set with Bren, who signaled to me that she wanted to continue seeing each other. But I had made my choice. It was Marta.

What choice would THAT girl make now about us?

I waited two days to call her. I was ashamed that I had hurt her. I was less worried about her breaking up with me than I was about her crying in her room because her boyfriend was an ass.

She would not talk to me. I waited two more days and called again. She still would not talk to me. I called the next day.

Her sister, Greta, again answered the phone, but this time instead of saying, "She doesn't want to talk with you," she said, "What the hell is wrong with you?" I had no answer for that question. She wasn't really looking for one. She already knew.

Marta finally came to the phone one day. I had mapped what I would say because I knew how this could go, and I at least wanted to see her and talk with her, even if she said goodbye.

"Marta, I am so sorry. I really want to talk with you, but not on the phone. I want to tell you face-to-face that I am sorry. If you want to break up with me, it would hurt, but I would understand."

She was silent, then said OK. It was a tone of defiance, anger, hurt and perhaps more than anything, still, disbelief.

She agreed to meet me the next day at the lake where I had gone so often with the guys. It was my suggestion, but she would not let me pick her up. So I told her where I would meet her on the hill overlooking the shoreline of this small recreational lake.

I thought a lot about what it meant to be a boyfriend, and I realized that coming up with fresh ideas to have fun together, opening doors for her, complimenting her on clothes she has made … that this was not all that it meant to be a boyfriend. Not only are you there for her always, you never hurt her, ever.

***

Becky Price stands at our table. "Hello Tom," she says.

Tom looks at her but he makes no sudden move, then he does stand to see her, face-to-face.

"Becky Price," he smiles, and bows. I know he is unsure how to respond, so he responds as he has with everyone tonight, with a smile and a laugh and a name. Then he makes a decision: no more guarded uncertainty. "I can't tell you," he says to her, "how good it is to see you."

Becky is radiant. There is no ring on her finger. I suspect that I am not the only one at our table to notice.

"You remember Nick Taylor."

"Of course. It's nice to see you, Nick."

I doubt she recognizes me any more than anyone else tonight. "And it's nice to see you, Becky."

Tom turns to me, a secret smile.

"Hey, uh, I'm going to get some more appetizers," I get up from the table. "Can I get you anything? Becky? Tom?" I start to leave them to each other.

"Hey Taylor," Tom says, and I turn around as Becky sits down. "Hold that thought," is all he says.

***

I am holding my breath.

It was Monday, September 2, 1968, Labor Day weekend. Senior year will start soon. The lake—where for years as kids and teens all the boys in our neighborhood cavorted in summer and gawked at the pretty girls seemingly beyond our reach—was packed.

I went early to find a spot. I parked my 1964 Ford Falcon with its 170 cubic inch engine and three on the tree. I found an open spot where I said I would be. I put a blanket down and waited.

Even the seconds seemed like hours. All I could do was wait.

I saw her just before she saw me. I waved to her.

She sat on my blanket and looked at me. A mixture again of hurt that I had caused and defiance which was her response. My time with the girl I had dreamed about for most of the decade hung in the balance, but regardless of what happened, I was going to make this right with her.

"I know it seems so small given what I said to you, but I want to tell you how sorry I am. I cannot believe I said such things to a girl I like so much, but I did, and I am sorry."

She looked at me. Seconds now seemed like days. For once, I knew, this was not about me. Her face suddenly softened, "I know." Silence. Then ... "I need to know," she continued, then paused. "What kind of man," she finally asked me, "*are* you?"

I sighed and looked at her. I did not know the look on my face. I only knew the consternation in my heart and mind and soul. "I don't know ...."

It was the most honest thing I had ever said in my life.

"But I am going to find out ... because I let my temper get the best of me with the one person in the world I never want to hurt. I have to change. I *will* change."

She had already made her decision. It turned out that what I said and perhaps what I did not say confirmed it in her mind.

"I know," she said, then smiled.

Whatever we had before was no comparison to what we had after that. Our relationship blossomed, deepened. We were in love, but neither of us had ever been in love before, so we did not realize it.

And we never actually said it to each other. We just said, *I like you sooooooo much!* In some ways, we were so unbelievably naive, but it was true.

At the stroke of midnight as December 31, 1968 turned into January 1, 1969, Hubert Humphrey got up from watching TV with his wife, Muriel, went to the bathroom and flushed the toilet.

The year 1968 was that bad, and not just for Humphrey. It remains one of the worst years in the history of the USA.

But not for me.

1968 was the best year of my life. At least up to that point.

Chapter 17

"For What It's Worth"

Tom and Becky are still talking, laughing now. As I watch from the bar, she reaches out and touches his arm as they sit together. Maybe there is no statute of limitations on this first love, or maybe they are just enjoying some time together again.

My wife, when we were dating, asked me about my first love and averred she had none, just a series of dates starting when she was thirteen. Hard to believe, but I believe her. Except maybe for that guy from Japan she dated for a year until his employer sent him home to Tokyo to prevent any possibility of marriage with an American. That was in 1969.

When I told her about mine, that we had dated through high school and into college, and that she lived in the neighborhood, my wife labeled her as, "the dog next door."

Decades later, when for some reason we were talking about past boyfriends and girlfriends, she looked at me and said, "I don't think you ever get over your first love."

Maybe, maybe not, but I say no ghosts are haunting me.

"Doesn't matter," she says. "I'm the one who won."

Maybe, maybe not. What kind of prize did she win?

Maybe, maybe not. Will I ever see Tom Baker again?

I bump into Jim Hanson. He is one of the surprisingly few other classmates who are bald—although he does not shave his head as I do—but otherwise he looks the same as in high school. Even though we did not know each other, I know who he is.

"Hey Jim, how are you?"

We shake hands.

I ask him if he still lives in the area.

No, he lives in Columbus.

I ask, did you go to Ohio State and stay?

Yes, he married a local girl.

I say, are you retired?

Yes, he sold his landscaping company.

I say, how did you get into landscaping?

And now he comes alive.

He was a horticulture major at Ohio State and entered landscape architecture. He worked for a local landscaper then started his own company, then bought a competitor but lost business when that owner left the combined company. He sold before he could be forced into bankruptcy, rebuilt his finances, and started another one. He expanded but kept it under control and sold it on retirement.

I tell him a little about my history and we go our separate ways.

Everyone has a story. I am always curious, and I find every one of them interesting in its own way. And of course, now I can tell my wife the extrovert just how many people I have talked with tonight. Almost everyone! Well, a dozen.

Yes, I am indeed keeping score. Extroverts have *no* idea how hard this is.

After my interaction with Jim, it occurs to me that not a single song, book, movie, or most of all, memory floods my mind. My conscious mind finds it hard to believe that my subconscious mind is momentarily at rest.

I did not know Jim at all in school, so talking with Jim does not resurrect a single memory.

And that is fine with me.

The past is a nice place to visit now and then, but I wouldn't want to live there all the time.

Sort of like New York.

Chapter 18

"Summer of '69"

"That's one small step for man—"
Neil Armstrong is stepping on the moon. Then everybody yells in unison, "one giant leap for mankind!!!" "Hey," yells Chuck Long, "how'd you all know he'd say that?!" And we all laugh.

It is Saturday, July 20, 2019, the 50th class reunion for our high school class of 1969, and the 50th anniversary of the Apollo 11 mission to the moon, when Neil Armstrong then Buzz Aldrin walked on the moon while Michael Collins remained in lunar orbit.

The reunion committee is streaming highlights of 1969. What better event to feature than the moon landing on the same date.

Yeah, I think, as everyone returns to their chats and drinks, we all know what Armstrong said in becoming the first man to step onto the surface of the moon. Armstrong was wondering just how far his boots would sink in the dust. Not far, as it turned out.

Everybody else around the world was wondering just what the first words of the first man on the moon would be. Armstrong later said he really did not know for sure what he would say until he said it. He had, after all, been a little busy.

But I remember what Aldrin said too when he stepped off the

ladder onto the surface of the moon. "Beautiful view ... magnificent desolation."

In a way, that was *my* summer of '69. Magnificent desolation.

It was a beautiful summer, but with a train of events that had never happened before, and it was often a runaway train.

The moon landing did what seemingly nothing else could. It united the country—and maybe the world—for a day, on what man could achieve and made us forget to hate.

"Get Together" by The Youngbloods pops into my mind. Yeah ... one small step for all of us, and then it was gone ....

Then the music festival that followed did what seemingly nothing else could: it united people for a few days (and not just one day) on how man could create beauty and make us remember to live.

"Going up the Country" by Canned Heat pops into my head. Yeah, who wouldn't go where the water tastes like wine? I think it's in New England somewhere ....

My summer was a beautiful view looking at the past, but there was magnificent desolation thinking of the future.

Because I was absolutely terrified.

Will I ever forget anything? No. Now I feel like Forrest Gump.

I stand at the monitor at the reunion and watch the moon landing *again* ... and I remember that weekend ....

It was Saturday, July 19, 1969. I had been listening about some place called Chappaquiddick, something about Ted Kennedy and a woman in a car in the water off a bridge.

Marta was talking to me on the phone. We were invited to the Kilkennys to watch the moon landing the next afternoon, but I was distracted, listening to the news on the radio.

"Wait ... Steve said his family was inviting us to ... what? Oh the moon landing. What time?"

Steve and Marta talked all the time. I was not worried. They were good friends. I was hearing her but not listening. The news was captivating ... it was, after all, the career I intended to pursue.

I observed both the event and the coverage, and I first thought of how Ted Kennedy years before suffered a broken back because of a plane crash, and now suffered an automobile accident. How is he— what more could this family take?

The day progressed. News about the accident darkened: the woman was dead, drowned in the car, and he survived, late at night, after a party. Married men, single women. More will come out—a supposed wrong turn on a road the senator had driven, with a driver, earlier that day, on an island his family had visited for years. What really happened? It was, as this historic weekend progressed, one of the topics for astronaut wives to discuss who had so much time, waiting.

"And tonight? We're still set for the movies?" I wanted to see *Once Upon a Time in the West.* She wanted to see *Funny Girl.* Marta and Steve love Streisand. I am indifferent.

Oddly, I married a girl who likes Streisand even *more.*

Both movies were playing at local drive-in theaters long after their release dates, one reason I associate many movies from the Sixties with the year I saw them and not when they came out.

So, *Funny Girl* it was.

Once Upon a Time in the West ... I muse about that movie as I look around at my classmates. It is still my favorite movie. *Funny Girl* is—of course it is—funny, but it is sad as Fanny Brice and Nick Arnstein separate. Marta did not know that it was the ending to the fairy tale, and she was upset. She still could not handle failed romances.

***

I watch the monitor.

"Beautiful view ... magnificent desolation."

Buzz Aldrin has stepped on the surface of the moon. Seems I am the only classmate still watching. I know this streaming coverage has been edited, deftly, I conclude, because it appears Aldrin closely follows Armstrong down the steps and to the moon, but in reality, it is nineteen minutes between Armstrong and Aldrin.

Moreover, it is more than six hours between the time the men land and the time they walk on the moon, but what is on this monitor is seamlessly woven so there is little time between these events.

Time travel.

Buzz, you may not be the first person to step foot on the moon, but this time, everybody remembers who came in second. You will always be a winner.

***

"What do you think Neil Armstrong is going to say?!" Randy Kilkennny was excited. He was ten, but we were all excited, just as excited as a ten-year-old boy. We should be.

"I don't know, Randy," I said. "That's what everyone is talking about right now. What do *you* think he's going to say?"

Randy smiled. "Maybe he'll quote something from Jules Verne!"

Everybody laughed.

"Well," I said, "wouldn't that be something? But a lot of people are suggesting what he should say. In fact," I grinned, "I read that Muhammad Ali said he hopes they bring back someone from the moon for him to fight because he's beaten everybody on earth."

Everybody laughed again.

I watch the monitor.

Ali really did say that to *Esquire*, which at the time was one of the nation's preeminent magazines. Its July 1969 issue interviewed a raft of notables on what Armstrong should say.

John Kenneth Galbraith: "We will have to pave the damn thing." I would not have expected putative levity from an economist. Unsurprisingly, it wasn't funny.

Isaac Asimov: "Goddard, we are here!" I knew it was a reference to Robert Goddard, who first used liquid fuel to fire rockets. Just too esoteric.

Bob Hope: "It really is made of green cheese!" I always thought his writers let him down on this one.

Gwendolyn Brooks: "Here there shall be peace and love." The poet sounded like Jackie DeShannon, who that summer sang what the world needed was just love.

William O. Douglas: "I pledge that we the people of earth will not litter, pollute and despoil the moon, as we have our own planet." It was not what one would expect from a Supreme Court justice, but it was as hopeful.

I knew all this at the time when we watched the moon landing and walk at the Kilkennys, but even then I was reluctant to share what I knew, even with those closest to me.

The coverage began at noon. The last time I could recall such continuous coverage was the JFK assassination.

I watch the monitor.

I know that the network coverage will run for some 30 hours.

At least, I think, there was none of that stupid music that news media now play with their "special coverage" of major events.

Cronkite and CBS had more than 30 remote locations from around the US and another thirteen in nations around the world. They were prepared for interviews and stories throughout the night.

"Hey, they're going to land!" Steve was as excited as his little brother. We gathered around the television in the living room. It was shortly after 4 p.m. Sunday, July 20, 1969. The lunar module slowly descended toward the surface of the moon. And at 4:17 p.m., the lunar module landed on the moon.

Armstrong, not yet walking on the moon, spoke: "Houston … from Tranquility Base … the Eagle has landed."

"Man on the moon!" Walter Cronkite crowed. Walter Cronkite at 52 was as excited as Randy Kilkenny at ten.

"Man on the moon!" Randy Kilkenny crowed.

I watch the monitor.

It is shortly after 4 p.m. I know that Armstrong takes the helm as the automatic controls threaten to dump the craft into boulders on the surface. At 4:17:40 p.m., with only seconds of fuel left for the landing on the moon, Armstrong safely plants the craft on the moon. It is some distance from where the computers would have put them.

"Houston ... Tranquility Base here ... The Eagle has landed."

"Oh boy," says Cronkite. He takes off his glasses, rubs his hands together in glee.

There are huge screens erected in cities around the world, like in Trafalgar Square in London, for people to watch, and for the moment, Cronkite, a fan of the space program, is one of us in the hundreds of millions watching and celebrating.

"Roger, Tranquility ... we copy you on the ground."

"You've got a bunch of guys about to turn blue ... we're breathing again ... thank you."

Gene Kranz, their flight director, is one of the guys being thanked. Kranz famously said, "failure is not an option," in willing Mission Control to get a crippled Apollo 13 home the following spring of 1970.

Kranz is relieved and so free to be irritated, and is no less pithy in a comment that is not as well remembered: "Tell Armstrong," he growled, "that there is no god damn gas station on the moon."

"You are STAY," Mission Control tells Armstrong and Aldrin that all systems indicate no problems. If there had been any, the astronauts would have been ordered to lift off the moon.

"Be advised ... there are a lot of smiling faces down here ... and all over the moon."

"There are two of them up here," replies Aldrin.

"And don't forget one in the command module!" adds Collins.

Mike Collins, the forgotten man.

I think about Mike Collins as I watch. He did not have the opportunity to walk on the moon with Armstrong and Aldrin, but that's not why I think about him.

Mike Collins married Pat Finnegan in 1957. I knew that she was Catholic, and he was not. That was a big issue then, or could be. Frequently one was advised, if not expected, by parents to marry within your race *and* your religion. I know I was, on religion.

In the end, it didn't matter to him.

As summer started in 1969, it didn't matter to me either that Marta was Catholic and I was Baptist. But by the end of that summer, it was becoming a dealbreaker.

Yeah, Mike Collins was never a forgotten man to me.

"I never thought I would live to see the day," said Mr. Kilkenny.

We were watching and waiting, the Kilkenny family and us, for Armstrong and then Aldrin to emerge from the module.

"When are they supposed to walk on the moon?" Debbie asked.

Nobody knew for sure, so we watched, mostly Cronkite and CBS. Occasionally Mr. Kilkenny instructed one of the kids to get up and change the channel to NBC or ABC and then back to CBS. Cronkite was a bigger star than the astronauts, for now.

But the three networks, all powerful, knew when to expect the moon walk. They were prepared with interviews around the country and world—interviews with other astronauts about the moon suits Armstrong and Aldrin were wearing and what Collins did during this time, chats with scientists on the value of the enterprise and more.

There was a lot of space and time to fill, just like there is today when news media are all talk all of the time.

One of the more interesting pieces to me is a sidebar story on Rev. Ralph Abernathy, who commented that money spent on the space program would be better spent on feeding poor people. Chet Huntley of NBC, voicing his opinion, agreed.

But NBC co-anchor David Brinkley had his mind elsewhere. "They finally find a place where there is no picket with a sign that says 'Get Out of Vietnam' or 'Yankee Go Home.'"

It will be more than six hours between the landing and the walk on the moon. We kept the television running in the background but slowly turned elsewhere. We older teens played cards.

Because the Kilkennys were a large family with many mouths to feed, including those—like us—who were not part of the family, my mom told me to take snacks with me. I had stopped at a convenience chain to get ham, cheese, bread, potato chips, chip dip, several cartons of pop and wafer cookies with a light sugar paste between two layers. It was part of our feast as we played cards, first euchre and then hearts. It was a long six hours.

We were idling as we waited for the walk on the moon ....

Similarly, most days that summer I was idling ... waiting in line to enter the lake park on just another early summer day. I knew I held on to high school as long as possible, even days earlier telling myself, *you're still in high school, you're still in high school,* awaiting my diploma at graduation.

It took me so long to figure out who I was and what I could do in high school. Junior year was the best, insulated from the future for another whole year, no real worries as long as the grades stayed up. I did not have to think about college, marriage, career.

I was prepared to get a job that summer but my dad told me to take the summer off. Once you start working, he said, you'll be working for the next forty years. He was only short by four.

I had a lot of space and time to fill. I was devoid of responsibility except regular chores like sweeping the house, shaking the rugs, washing the porch and the cars, so I filled my time and my mind with anything that I could. And one way was to lounge at the lake. I would spread out a beach towel and sit and read. My dad had a trove of westerns written by Zane Grey, Luke Short, Louis L'Amour and others, and I read them all.

I knew that Eisenhower had read similar dime-store novels as they were called, to take his mind off the war. It worked for me, too, but only as long as my nose was stuck in a book. If my time and my mind were not occupied, they were quickly preoccupied with anxiety around starting college in the fall.

I had heard too many stories about college course work, of getting assignments to read 300 pages before the next class, and I was terrified that I might fail.

When I started college that fall, my fears were confirmed when on the first day, a professor gave an assignment to read 200 pages before the next class. I sat on my bed in misery at the end of the day. I was never going to make it. Then I realized that I would not see that class and professor for two more days. I had the time that I needed.

But that anxiety was manifested for years after college, in dreams in which I would awake in fear I had not completed assignments due that day. I was over 30 years old before it stopped.

I put the westerns down every hour or so and swam. I needed the exercise. In boredom, I ate, and there was a freezer full of mini sandwiches left over from the graduation party my folks had held.

But it was different from the past, when all of us teenage boys in the neighborhood would play tag on the docks for hours. Others were working summer jobs or heading to boot camp and it was just me now, and a lake full of people I did not know.

Somehow I got hooked on *Dark Shadows*, the soap opera with a vampire and a werewolf and more. But I spent most of my days with the Baker twins, who had a business cleaning banks (their dad was a bank executive) at night, and the three of us ran around all summer. They always knew the coolest music, stuff I would never have taken time to hear, like Arlo Guthrie and the "Motorcycle Song," where *pickle*, *tickle*, and *motorcycle* all rhymed. Hey, why not? This wasn't exactly Mantovani, you know.

Marta worked at the mall—she worked a lot of hours saving for college—so we might visit the Kilkennys, we might see a movie, or more likely we would just watch television at her house. Summer nights usually ended with a bit of kissing before we said goodnight, usually in my car in her driveway. We listened to a lot of music in my car in her driveway that summer.

"Baby I Love You" by Andy Kim and "Working on a Groovy Thing" by The 5th Dimension pop into my head from driveway makeout songs. The only time we said I love you to each other was when we sang it as the lyrics in these songs.

It was a desultory summer. I listened to Marvin Gaye sing when it comes to thinking about his baby, he ain't got time for nothing else. I had *too* much time to think about the future. I stayed up late every night, just to hope the summer would never end.

Much like Christmas Eve when no matter where I had been or what I had done with my girlfriend or family earlier in the evening, I stared for hours at the lights on the Christmas tree—the silver artificial tree with a color wheel flashing yellow, blue, green and red—just to make the night last. It was a false dawn.

The terror spiked when I had to attend freshman orientation at Kent just before the moon landing. Freshman were required— forced is more like it—to spend two days on campus in myriad classes and sleep in a dorm with other incoming frosh.

Most of our time was spent in a lecture hall with no air-conditioning, so the windows were open and now and then a breeze wafted through. So did "Good Morning Starshine" by Oliver.

I half-listened to the orientation as it droned—I never could suffer bureaucracy of any kind—and half-listened to a pop tune with silly lyrics, and it was better, a *lot* better.

One night in a dorm with two other guys was enough to convince me there was no way that I was living in a dorm. It reminded me of the Yuma Territorial Prison from the Old West, only prison was nicer. I would commute to school every day rather than deal with that insanity. I am a closet claustrophobic. The room was too confining, but mostly it was just the presence of other people and one dorm mate, Tim Smith, was crazy.

"Are you eighteen?" he asked.

"Yes I am," I replied.

"Can I borrow your ID?"

"... No."

The other, Dom Ricci, was cool. In the spare time allotted to us, he and I wandered campus and talked about starting in the fall. He was also nervous about college, which made me feel better.

Twenty-five years later, I worked on a public relations account whose main contact was Mario Ricci. I asked if he had a brother named Dom, and he did. Mario was shocked that I would remember, perhaps wondering if I had snooped into his personal life. Dom remembered me, if not my name, so Mario and I were cool.

Another reason I rarely flash *the memory* is that it makes people too easily suspicious, or it just freaks them out and makes them think that I might be some sort of weird government experiment.

It was 11 p.m. Marta and I were ready to leave and at the door. It did not look like the moon walk would happen that night, but then Steve called out, "Hey, come back, the hatch is opening."

We settled on the couch and watched, transfixed, as was most of mankind as Neil Armstrong finally stepped off the ladder.

"One small step for man ... one giant leap for mankind."

Cronkite was so excited that he stated the obvious. "Armstrong is on the moon!" But who could blame him?

We watched for hours—the whole family—even the youngest, until Armstrong and Aldrin lifted off to reunite with Collins.

Mission Control was worried. There were two scenarios that could not be rehearsed: one was the landing, which while it succeeded did so with only seconds of fuel left; and then there was takeoff, which would take even more fuel, but it worked out as planned.

Television anchors complained that there was not enough chatter among the astronauts, as if this were a made-for-television movie.

As one of the wives said to others with her watching the entire event, that is what makes these guys good at their job.

Then Cronkite again stated the obvious: "What a day!"

I watch the monitor.

"Beautiful view ... magnificent desolation."

What a summer.

Chapter 19

Tom and Becky are still talking and laughing.

I sigh. How much more can I talk? Extroverts have no idea how lucky they are. I feel like I have run a marathon.

"Perseverance!"

I start laughing before I even turn around and I know before I move and before he laughs too that it is Andy Longstreet.

"Andy Longstreet!"

"Nick Taylor!"

We do the guy hug, the pat on the back thing, do not get too close. I still do not understand the guy hug, but then again, I do not like hugging, and avoid hugging if possible.

"Hi my name is Nick, and I have a problem ... I hate hugging."

Andy Longstreet played sax in the junior high band, abdicating with Mike Hawkins at the start of high school when their band became popular enough to take gigs outside of school dances. But not before the three of us and Bill Wolf participated in what was until then, and perhaps remains, the biggest competitive debacle in the history of our junior high school band.

"Andy, I *still* think of that day now and then."

"Yeah, Nick, me too. Still hard to believe ...."

"And when you used that word in a response to a post that I made on Facebook, well, I just lost it, Andy."

And we laugh some more.

Andy, Mike, Bill, and I were in a saxophone quartet participating in a regional band competition. Judges were band directors from nearby counties. If they are alive, they are still in shock.

We knew the material relatively well although there had been little opportunity to practice. But in the end, that wasn't the problem. Within seconds of our performance, Bill suffered a split reed and could barely play. And he was the best of the four of us.

Mike and Andy, consumed with practice in their nascent band, had barely practiced this material apart from us and counted on us. Then the glue holding the pads in place on my aging sax—the same one I had used since the fourth grade—failed, and the pads literally began to fall off, leaving me with only shrieking sounds.

We were so bad that being awful would have been good.

We started laughing as soon as we went outside, and then our band director, Walter Pierce, came to the picnic table where we were sitting and laughing. He was a nice man, although chubby, particularly rotund in the middle. He was an excellent band director.

One day earlier that year, Bill said to me, "Do you know what his nickname is?"

"No, what?"

Bill laughed before he even spoke. "Pear!" I laughed in spite of myself but never called him that name.

Pierce was not amused as he approached our foursome. "Here ... I hope you're all proud of yourselves." He handed us a paper with our grade. It was astonishing.

There were two columns: on the first column, which even now seems as if it filled the entire page, was a list of our sins. It covered everything we did wrong, and it was right.

"Faulty equipment. Poor grasp of material. Out of tune. Need more practice." Well, yeah, that list seemed endless and obvious to us.

On the other column, positives, there was just a single word. "Perseverance."

We were not sure if the judges laughed as hard as us when they wrote that word, or if they had simply struggled to find any positive word, and settled on that one. But that was right, too.

Andy raises his beer and we clink bottles.

"Perseverance!"

I am a step behind. "Perseverance!"

"Hey," I add, "you have a big anniversary coming up."

"Yeah," he replies, "coming up on 26 years."

I stop raising my beer in another toast. "I thought you got married in the fall of '69 and you were still married. Oh shit …."

"First part is right," he laughs, "but not the second. At least not to that one … 26 years this fall, to the *right* one!"

"Geez, I'm really sorry, Andy …"

Usually I have the facts right, but as they used to say in the newsroom, never let the facts stand in the way of a good story.

He smiles and shakes his head. "It's no big deal, Nick."

***

"It's a big deal, Nick."

Marta was talking about houses. I was again distracted, listening to the news on the radio.

It was Saturday, August 16, 1969. I had been listening to stories about someplace called Woodstock and how organizers had expected 200,000 but 400,000 showed up. And about the latest on the murders the previous weekend of Sharon Tate and others. And about a hurricane called Camille.

Things seemed to happen in bunches that summer of '69.

"Wait, your parents are looking at houses tomorrow. The … what is it? Parade of homes? OK, sure, I'll go with you."

***

"We are great, we are fine, we're the class of '69!"

A cheer arises on the other side of the room. More bottles and glasses clink. Andy and I look over at our classmates.

"It really was a great class, wasn't it?" Andy says.

"I think you're right," I respond. "It was a great class."

Andy looks back at me. "But it was a really weird year."

I know that Andy has had more than a few weird years.

He lost a grandson to the opioid epidemic for example and is relentlessly pressing legislators to address the problem. I know this from his frequent posts about the opioid crisis, on Facebook and other social media where I have connected with a dozen or so classmates, some I really did not know well.

Andy and I run into each other now and then at restaurants and bars, and he always has a smile. It is in his eyes, too.

If the face is an index to the mind, then the eyes are an index to the soul. Faces can lie but eyes, not so much. When my wife and I watch interviews on television, the eyes are our initial test of believability. If we think a person has what we simply call "kind eyes," we are more likely to listen to what that person has to say.

I first applied this criterion as a reporter when I studied the eyes of people in interviews. Similarly, I used it when preparing executives for interviews in peacetime or wartime.

"Let's stop here," I would say when the words did not match the eyes in a training session, and for example, tell the executive: "I can tell from your facial expressions, and particularly your eyes, that you may not be sure about the answer. Am I right? But you are still trying to answer the question."

Corporate leaders sometimes think they are expected to know everything about a topic or a situation, and it's not possible.

"That will get you into trouble, ten times out of ten. If you don't know the answer to a question, just say you don't know."

Sometimes, I would echo what corporate communications chiefs told their executives. Sometimes, I would tell the executives what the corporate communications chiefs were afraid to say.

I was prepping a CFO for interviews as the company, an airline, planned a bankruptcy filing in Manhattan. The PR team were terrified of him, said he eats people for breakfast. So our first drill was the two of us in a face-off, with my camera man right behind my shoulder. He turned the lights on full blast and I shoved the mic at the CFO and said, *"Mr. Collins, what just happened in that courtroom?"*

He was startled, and then guffawed. He listened to everything I told him would happen and how to handle it, even taking me with him to the New York offices of the bankruptcy lawyers where he sat me next to him at the head of the table, and then into the courtroom and finally out to the television cameras.

The PR team thought it miraculous. How could I get their guy to listen to me when he rarely listened to anyone else?

He was sharp, smart and tough, but he had kind eyes, too. I could tell him what he wanted to hear, or I could tell him what he needed to hear. There was never, in my career, any doubt.

If an executive said that I was tougher on them than any of the media, then I knew I had done my job. I always thought it weird that people are afraid to say what needs to be said. You do the right thing, always.

Weird the word, has sparked this side-conversation in my head. But what, I think, is weird about that? Happens all the time.

"Yeah," I say. "It was a really weird year all right."

Andy has a coda to this conversation. "Was there ever a year like that one?"

***

"Was there ever a year like this one?" Marta asked.

Marta and I were in the back seat, headed with her parents to tour the parade of homes. It was a subdivision of new homes in an eastern suburb of Akron. It was the day, the weekend, when hundreds of thousands waited out the rain for the music at Woodstock.

It was Sunday, August 17, 1969.

Mr. Mecklenberg considered the question from his daughter. I learned later that her parents knew what she really meant. "I'd have to think about that one," he said and reflected as he drove.

"Maybe 1960, when Kennedy was elected. Big change for the country with the first president born in this century. He was also the first Catholic to become president ....

" ... Maybe 1945, with the end of the war and the atomic bomb ... I remember that like it was only yesterday ....

" ... Or maybe 1927 ... I was eight ... with Lindbergh crossing the Atlantic ... I remember listening to the news on the radio ....

" ... Or maybe 1945 ... when Ilsa and I got married."

Mr. and Mrs. Mecklenberg laughed then added, "Maybe there haven't been many like this ... maybe there hasn't ever been a year like this ... man on the moon ... we watched it all on TV ..."

"We watched the whole thing too, at the Kilkennys," I said.

We tour all of the homes, except those beyond a certain price point, and focus longest on those within a smaller range, some twice, all freshly appointed.

I do my best to appear interested. We head to the car.

"That's about the best we can do," said Mr. Mecklenberg.

It was not until later, when Marta and I were in the car heading to the Kilkennys to play cards, that I asked about it. "I didn't know your parents were thinking about moving," I said.

I still did not get it ... I was about to learn of the conspiracy.

"They're not thinking about moving," she smiled at me. "They were looking at houses for us."

I looked sharply at her.

"I told you," I was emphatic and perhaps overly loud, "We are *not* getting married until after we graduate from college." We had talked about marriage, but we were not engaged.

"Look, I am sorry if I overreacted," I said. I did not want to hurt her. But we were not getting married right out of high school.

There was quiet. We were silent. What was there to say?

***

Joe Cocker is singing The Beatles on the reunion playlist.

"With a Little Help From My Friends" … *Cocker at Woodstock. Nobody was going to walk out on this one, even in rain.*

"I heard him sing this, you know," Andy says.

"You heard Joe Cocker sing this? Where?"

"Woodstock." Andy grins, what used to be called a shit-eating grin.

Wait, what? "You … were at WOODSTOCK?" I am incredulous. I make it a point to know everything if I can about everything, everyone, but not today. How did I not know this? People wear such things as a badge, yet I have never heard him talk about it.

"Yes I was!"

"OK, give—you have to tell me about it, Andy!"

"Well, I went with a bunch of guys who had a band. I played with them when they needed me, and we played all over the area. One of them had a cousin in upstate New York and we went there earlier in the week. So we were there early and right from the start of the festival when Richie Havens came out and played—"

Andy is silent. He is remembering. I do not interrupt.

But I know Havens sang "Freedom," and that he was on stage for some three hours that first night because there was no one else that could perform.

Andy is talking and I hear the songs he heard. I *know* who played there, I *know* what they sang there. I knew that Havens was not supposed to play until later, but it was not only the people going to the festival who were stuck in the traffic—which stretched 15 miles— but also the performers. Sweetwater was supposed to go first but were nowhere near the stage, stuck in traffic.

The promoters looked for people without much equipment and that meant acoustic guitars. They even pressed John Sebastian into playing, and he was just there to watch. He was backstage because he knew everyone and wanted to watch and learn.

"Darlin' Be Home Soon" by John Sebastian pops into my head.

He sang that at Woodstock.

Country Joe McDonald was there without his band (with whom he was supposed to perform another day). McDonald said later that people were really not paying much attention to him until he yelled out, "Give me an F ..." and then the crowd followed the entire chant and song.

"Havens was unbelievable," Andy said. "Especially when he started singing 'Freedom' ... we all went wild."

There are winners and losers in everything. Sweetwater was one of the losers and Havens one the winners. Because of traffic.

"We never had to deal with that traffic, just the people. We stayed to the end. We didn't leave until Jimi Hendrix played the "Star Spangled Banner." But the rain Friday night, it rained five inches in three hours ... didn't matter what you did, you got soaked."

I think about the comment made by novelist Ayn Rand: "*Left to their own devices, they literally didn't know when to come in out of the rain ....*" And the editorial board of *The New York Times* sniffed, "*What kind of culture can produce so colossal a mess?*"

But when reporters who had been at Woodstock threatened to quit over this response, *The Times* backed down, sort of.

Suddenly I think, is it any wonder our generation turned away for a while? But then once the war was over, college students went back to cramming themselves into telephone booths and stuff.

"It was like it just would not stop. It would stop for a bit and then start again ... like, Joe Cocker sings his set 'With a Little Help From My Friends' and it was fantastic, but Cocker looked like he was having a heart attack and then it rains again."

Yeah, everybody stayed to listen to him tell a tale ... and, to my ears anyway, better than The Beatles ... not an easy thing to do.

"It was a mess, an absolute mess. All the people ... the rain, the mud, the heat ... you could take a bath, skinny dipping, in the pond on the property.

"If you lined up for the toilets, it was a test of how long you could hold your breath, the smell was so bad. And most people ran out of water and food. There was a group from the West Coast called the Hog Farm that gave out food. First time I ever had granola. They were even teaching people yoga ... first time I ever did yoga, too.

"At one point, Janis Joplin told the crowd, 'If you have any food left, give it to your brother and sister ... your brother and sister are on your left and on your right ....'

"Piece of My Heart" by Janis Joplin plays in my head... but there is suddenly a heretical lyric rattling around in my head. Yeah, take another little piece of my sandwich, baby ....

Andy laughs, remembering, "There were supposed to be some concession stands but really there wasn't much food. One of the guys said, 'We could get balled ...'" he laughs again, "when's the last time you heard *that* word? ... 'we could get balled easier than we could get a bagel.'"

Yeah, Bethel, New York, is not exactly the deli capital.

"There was so much marijuana, you could go some places, Nick, like the woods where most of the drugs were sold, and you could get high just walking around."

Yeah, coffee houses in Amsterdam are like that too.

"There was even a 'Bad Trips Tent' that was set up for anyone who got strung out. Some bands had to be careful putting any amps on stage because of the weather. Maybe it was the logistics, how hard it was to get all the equipment there and set up, but a lot of the music was disappointing. Not all of it, Joe Cocker was good, Santana was fantastic, CCR played great stuff, but nothing that came out that fall like 'Fortunate Son.'"

"Born on the Bayou" by CCR pops into my head. Yeah ... so they didn't play "Fortunate Son" or "Willie and the Poor Boys," so what? "Born on the bayou ... don't let the man do you" ... Well those were pretty good lyrics too. Another anthem for me.

"Sly and the Family Stone, when they sang 'I Want to Take You Higher,' every time he sang 'higher,' all of us did too at the top of our lungs … *high-errrr!"*

"Boom shaka laka laka … boom shaka laka laka …." Memorable lyrics or what? Enough for Bill Murray and Harold Ramos to use in Stripes, *I guess.*

"By the time Hendrix closed out Monday morning, there were a lot fewer people. I heard there were only 50,000 left because so many people had left Sunday night, back to jobs, I guess."

Yeah, Jimi Hendrix closed out Woodstock … but I know that the organizers actually wanted Roy Rogers to sing "Happy Trails" at the end of the festival because we all grew up watching his show. But he said no. Really, why would he say yes?

Andy is the only person I have met who said he was at Woodstock and whom I believe, sort of like all those people who said they voted for George McGovern in 1972 or Hillary Clinton in 2016.

Listening to Andy as he recounts his four days of experiences in August 1969, without interruption from me, I am reminded that sometimes all you have to do is ask the right question.

***

"What about kids?"

It was late evening Monday, August 18, 1969. Woodstock was over, summer speeding toward denouement. Marta and I had talked about kids before, and more than once, but I had not properly phrased the question.

"I love kids, and I know you do too," she said.

"No. I know … I mean … What about church? What church would we raise our kids in?" After almost two years of dating, we knew we were serious about the future, and had talked through almost every issue, but not this one. Not directly, anyway.

I decided it was time to be definitive, both of us.

She looked at me and was amazed there was any question at all. "The Catholic Church," she said. "I want to raise my kids in my church, of course."

I already knew the answer before I asked the question. I nodded.

"I want to raise my kids in my church," I said.

There was silence in the car. We had turned off the radio.

"We don't have to discuss this right now," she finally said. "We can figure it out after we get married."

But I knew what that meant, and I knew that this was one subject on which we did not—and never would—agree.

"No," I smiled. "I guess you're right …."

I had hints where this was heading the entire time we dated. When she had to stay after school, I asked why. Catechism, she said. I said, *what?* I had never heard of this before.

"It's learning about the Catholic religion," she patiently explained. "Everyone goes through catechism. My kids will, too."

Marta had gone to my church. She sheepishly admitted to me afterward she was afraid I was spending so much time there because of a girl. And I had gone to her church, too.

Neither of us was much impressed with the other church.

We discussed religion many times. Maybe it is hard, I think, to understand how big an issue this was at the time. Maybe it still is. I don't know ….

Once when she and I were discussing religion, she had asked her mom about conversion to another faith. Her mom shocked her by saying she had converted from Baptist to Catholic when she married. Marta never knew this about her parents. She just looked at me.

I knew what she was thinking. I knew that it did not often happen the other way. I knew she would not convert to a different faith. I knew she expected me—as I knew so much about her religion—to be the one to convert.

"Love Can Make You Happy" by Mercy inevitably, I know, now playing in my head. A song that made me think of that summer.

Is love worth the price you pay if it makes you happy?

"If It Makes You Happy" by Sheryl Crow eclipses Mercy.

So which is the right question? Is love worth the price you pay? Or how bad can love be if it makes you happy?

For me right then, the right question, from a song, no less: Was it worth the price I would have to pay?

"Would you do it again?" I ask Andy.

Andy grins again.

"Woodstock?" he says. "In a New York minute!"

CHAPTER 20

"Something in the Air"

"**S**ugar, Sugar" by The Archies is on the reunion playlist.

Yeah ... playing in my head ... playing with my head ....

"So?"

Tom and Becky have parted, but only for the moment it turns out.

"So, what?"

"So, what's your answer?"

"First of all," I turn to face him, "I'm just sitting here listening to one of the greatest songs of all time." We both laugh. "And you're interrupting me, Baker. So, what question?"

"You know very well what question," he sits beside me.

"Well, let's do this, Baker. Since you just talked to the girl you *could* have married, you tell *me* what *you* said to Becky Price after all these years."

"Asps! Very dangerous. You go first."

Tom examines me, again with the narrowed eyes.

"Something" by The Beatles supplants "Sugar, Sugar" on the playlist.

"*That,*" Tom says, "is one of the greatest songs of all time."

Yeah, I think it was about Patty Boyd who was married at the time to George Harrison, who wrote the song ... Eric Clapton also wrote a song about her, "Wonderful Tonight."

"Sugar Sugar" was Don Kirchner using studio musicians for a manufactured chart topper to get even with the Monkees ... and prove he did not need a band to make hit records ...

STOP IT.

A little knowledge is a dangerous thing.

But not as dangerous as a lot of it can be ....

"You're stalling, man, tell me what you talked about with Becky."

"What do you think we talked about? We talked about our lives. What we've done in the last fifty years. What we've done with our lives. Dreams ... disappointments." Tom stopped. "She asked if I would be open to dinner."

He paused. I prompted, " And???"

"And ... we'll do dinner tomorrow night, while we're both still in town, before we head home."

I wait him out. I know there is more. It is an old reporter trick— stay silent—people cannot help themselves but talk.

Do I feel bad playing this reporter trick on a friend?

Not a chance in the world.

"It is nice to see her, nice to talk to her. You know, Taylor, I do not have a lot of regrets in my life," Tom pauses, then grimly smiles, "and Becky Price is not one of them. She can't be, given ... events ... but ... well, let's just leave it at that. It is nice to see her."

"So where does Becky Price live?"

"She lives in Seattle," he laughs, "not all that far for me. I have to get to Mount Hood for training. She wants me to stop by when I am up that way. So maybe I will."

"That's great, Tom."

He looks at me. "As for what we really talked about, I told her about my life helping kids, skiing just happens to be the backdrop. She point-blank asked why I never got married. And I told her ... I never really told her why I broke up with her... all those years ago, you know. I wasn't as honest as I should have been. But she knew ... she knew.

"She's got kids and grandkids. She's been divorced for a long time. She's retired. Worked at Microsoft. Lives alone …."

I've known Tom long enough to know that he is excited, maybe even hopeful. He deserves to be happy. I can only hope.

Tom is looking at me.

"OK, OK, this is going to sound like it's about you—I know you think everything is about you, Tom—but this time it is not." We both laugh. "What if, at nineteen, you make what you think at the time could be the biggest mistake you will ever make in your life …."

"You're right," Tom appears serious, "that does sound like me."

He smirks. I smile.

"So let me tell you a story. Some of it you already know. No one else knows this story, except my wife, and not all of it …."

"Do I need another beer?"

"You asked me a question, and I can't answer your question or mine until I tell you this story. So sit there and shut up, it's going to take a while."

Tom sits up, puts his elbow on the table, interlaces his fingers and tucks them under his chin and bats his eyes.

Once a smartass ….

It was the weekend after Labor Day, 1969, and THAT girl and I were heading to the Kilkennys. Still weeks from the start of school, my anxiety grew each day—not just about school.

Fall quarter, semesters came years later, started in late September. We had only just learned that she opted for life in the dorm while I opted for life in the car as a commuter.

I knew we would never agree on church and children. It had occurred to me over the Labor Day picnic with the Kilkennys that maybe—I hated myself for even considering the idea—but maybe she and I should break up, before we got to the point of being engaged or even married, or even expecting our first … and still had no agreement on this.

By the end of that week, I decided to break off our relationship…

and suggest that we should perhaps start seeing other people, too.

"Hey guys."

It is Betty Janes, swimming by again. I look at Tom. He is about to open his mouth. "Not a word, Baker. Not a word."

I planned to talk to Marta about it that weekend when I took her home, but I could not. I planned to talk to her about it the next weekend, but I could not get the words out of my mouth. I did not want to hurt her. What could I do? So for the first month of fall quarter, we continued as if nothing had happened. Because really, nothing had happened.

"You always did move fast, Taylor," Tom said.

She complained that she never saw me.

"Someone complained about not seeing you enough, Taylor? How often has that happened?"

"I seem to remember seeing you then more than I wanted," I said. "Every day in that commute across town to Kent."

It was while listening to Thunderclap Newman make money singing about a revolution that could never happen.

"Something in the Air"... Thunderclap Newman. Yeah ... there was something in the air all right in that late summer and early fall ... uncertainty ... what to do ....

And I knew I had to get it together now. The idea forming in my mind was that I would *make* her break up with me. Because then I would be the one who was hurting, and not her. The fact that she lived on campus and I did not could make it easier to pull this off. So I began to see her less, call her less, write her less.

But she increased her letters to me—two or three a week. Sometimes they were about classes, sometimes about roommates, and sometimes about college rituals, like panty raids.

Even as late as fall 1969, it seemed colleges were looking back more than ahead. We were given blue and gold beanies with little gold pins with blue lettering *Frosh '73.*

"You know what I remember most about the fall of 1969?" Tom

cannot help himself. "Tim, me and you walk onto campus that first day and there are 20,000 students, half of them girls and all of *them* in mini skirts. We thought we died and went to heaven."

"Ha. I remember us gawking at the girls," I rejoined, "but what I most remember is how different college was ... seeing chalked writing on the sidewalk that said 'Dick Nixon before he dicks you.'"

"Only you would remember Nixon over mini skirts, Taylor." Tom is constitutionally incapable of silence.

It did not happen right away, of course. She complained even more about missing me. We went back to normal over Thanksgiving break, but I hardly saw her afterward until Christmas break.

Between Christmas and New Year's, her friend Sunny, from the store at the mall where they both worked, was singing in a community production of *Oklahoma* in Wadsworth. We went. Sunny was spectacular. She was smart, too. Marta had told her she was worried about us, that she thought I was losing interest in her. Sunny said, *talk to him if you don't want to lose him.*

Marta was nervous. I was not sure why, but I knew she was not good at confrontation. I have learned almost no one is. I have since become adept at dealing with confrontation, which is simply dealing with problems directly and honest.

If I had been any good at it back then, I would have confronted her more directly about church and children. I thought I knew how it would turn out. Maybe I didn't.

After the performance, while we waited to congratulate Sunny, Marta asked me if everything was ok with us. I said, *I'm fine ... we're fine ... I'm just worried about school.*

Marta was palpably relieved.

But once winter quarter began, I started it up again. We saw each other even less as the new year started. We went to a concert—The Association—at the end of the first month back in class. When I took her back to the dorm, she said, I think we should date other people. I said, much to her obvious surprise, I think that's a great idea.

I congratulated myself all the way home.

The next day, it began to hit me what had happened. Or rather, to be honest, what I had done. That first week of February was terrible. She had made clear we should still date each other too. But I did not try at all. I had to let her go. I never talked to her at all.

You even urged me to send her flowers for Valentine's Day.

"I remember," Tom said. "I wondered why you didn't do it."

Toward the end of the month, she called me, and she never called me—guys usually did the calling then—she wanted to talk. We met at the student center and walked to her dorm, sitting in chairs in the lobby.

She said she was breaking up with me. My first thought was, *I thought you already had.* We talked. What we said is irrelevant now, but of course I remember every single thing we both said.

Then I paused in the telling of this story, thinking about those words...

I wished her a good life. I really didn't know what else to say, Tom. And then I walked away.

That winter seemed like it would never end. There were a lot of dark songs. 'Cold Kentucky Rain,' 'The Thrill is Gone'—

"The Rapper ...."

Very funny, Baker.

—Reflections of My Life' ... you remember them, no doubt.

March was tough. April, I could begin to see ... daylight ... I don't mean just sunlight. I mean daylight.

"Here Comes the Sun" by The Beatles pops into my head. Yeah, I listened to that song as much as I could that winter ... because it did seem like years since I had seen the sun.

But, I was moving on. I dated a couple of girls, but my heart was not in it. I never dated any of them more than twice ... until ... What do you do if at nineteen you make what you think at the time may be the biggest mistake you will ever make in your life ...

"Yeah," says Baker, perhaps thinking of himself now.

You hope you get lucky, I said. And that is exactly what happened to me when the girl who would become my wife came along. I thought that I had pushed away the love of my life. But it turns out that I had just found the love of my life.

So that's the story. I asked my question, and told you how it all worked out, but I haven't answered your question.

Tom studies me for a few seconds, pushing his lips out and in, out and in, as he ponders a story he has never heard. "Taylor," he starts, "either you're brilliant or you're a bonehead. OK, so now my question is," he says, "what would you say to her if she shows up here tonight at the reunion?"

"Attention everyone!" Jill Light has the mic in her hand. "Our buffet dinner will be served in ten minutes. Ten minutes!"

"Well," I tell Tom, "looks like a moot point." What would I say? "I am sorry if I ever hurt you, and thank you for what you did for me, all those years ago ..."

"That's it?"

I don't know, but what else is there to say?

"Well," I say to Tom, "it would depend, wouldn't it, on how the conversation between us were to go."

I know the art of saying something without saying anything. But...

"I was lucky, fortunate, to have the time with her ... and I was lucky to find another one who loves me and whom I love."

I feel like Forrest Gump ... *again*. *"That's all I have to say about that."*

"Maybe," says Tom, "*that* is what you say if you see her."

CHAPTER 21

"Things I'd Like to Say"

"*O*lder *then? Younger now?*"
"'My Back Pages' by The Byrds—"
"1967!"

I beat Tom on the song. I knew it before the lyrics even started. And the group. In fact, I knew the song at three notes ... but he slips in the year. I sorta let him save face.

Yeah, I *loved* that song in the spring of 1967, especially juxtaposed with, "When I Was Young" by The Animals. Because that spring, I felt that I was younger than before. I had worried about being accepted, about being part of the crowd ... and now I didn't care anymore. What they thought was irrelevant. What they thought of me was irrelevant too.

We are waiting now for the dinner announcement, and even Tom looks as if he has talked to enough classmates for a while. So in time-honored male fashion, we are matching memories to songs. It's a guy thing that even we don't understand.

"So is *that* the biggest mistake you will ever make in your life?"
"Dunno."
"Why not?"
"Not dead yet."

"Real funny, Taylor."

"OK, Tom, what's the biggest mistake you may have ever made, will have ever made, in *your* life?"

"That would be listening to you."

"How do they know? That it's time to go?"

"'Who Knows Where the Time Goes,' Fairport Convention 1969."

Tom looks annoyed.

"How in the world do you remember *that* song?"

I remember everything. And this time, I get the song in just two notes. If you cannot forget anything, then you do not count the time, because time never goes anywhere.

"Because of all the time listening to the radio when I sat in the car at Kent waiting for you and your brother to show up in the commuter lot so we could go home."

We commuted together for fall and winter quarters 1969-70 but broke the arrangement as schedules diverged in spring quarter. But driving with the Baker twins was always an adventure.

If I drove, they were never ready when I arrived at their house to pick them up. If they drove, they were always late picking me up at my house.

Either way, they usually got into fistfights on the expressway during rush hour traffic, even when one of them was driving. Either way, they were always late getting back to the car for the ride home … and already arguing about whose fault it was.

Once during winter quarter 1970, as we were leaving the commuter parking lot, Tim took a back road to the highway despite snowy and icy roads. When he came to a fork in the road, the car just kept going straight … into the embankment. There was momentary silence in the car. I was in the back and had hit my head on the roof of the car at the impact. There was no blood, just a bump.

Tim turned to Tom and said, "It's not my fault." Not, "Are you guys alright?" He never lived that down. Worse, neither of them had enough money for the tow truck, so I had to pay.

Although we stopped driving together, we spent time together the rest of our college careers, sometimes even by accident.

"Had it all? Without you?"

"Hamilton Camp, 'Here's to You,' 1967."

Tom just looks at me. It is the same look I get from my wife when I know something that beggars belief, and she says, "You ain't right." True for a lot more reasons than this one.

"Song was released in 1967 but if memory serves," my little joke, "it didn't get much airtime until fall 1968."

I don't flash *the memory* all that often ... even to friends ... less so to family. But now and then, I let the beast out to play.

Finally Tom just shakes his head. "I'm going to hit the head before dinner starts."

There he goes ...

"Off to write that hit song, 'alone in my principles' ...."

STOP IT.

Now I shake *my* head.

Once I am in the mode, it is really hard to get out of it. And when you remember every single thing, every single thing clamors for your attention.

I look around. People are slowly drifting to the dining tables. When Tom comes back, we'll follow the herd.

So. What *would* you say, what would *anyone* say, when they see their ex-girlfriend or ex-boyfriend—their first love—after like a century or so? Would you even say anything *at all?* Or maybe pretend you just don't see them? Would it be just too awkward to have to talk with them, one more time?

Raiders of the Lost Ark *pops into my head. Marian Ravenwood sees Indiana Jones for the first time in years. She always knew he'd come walking through her door again ... someday ... but what if someday never comes ....*

STOP IT.

I smile at that exchange. If it was a competition, Marian won. Men are not the stronger sex. Or the smarter sex, either. Duh.

Competition. I suspect that is what it often becomes.

I suspect that what most people would *like* to say, almost certainly what they *wish* they *would* say, is ….

"How Do You Like Me Now" by Toby Keith suddenly comes to mind and I laugh … *Yeah, well, even if I looked like I could say that and get away with it … I wouldn't say it to THAT girl … or anyone else …*

But the truth, I also suspect, is that it doesn't really matter what you would plan to say if you saw an ex-lover, or spouse, or first love, or the person who was all three. Because of the "fog of war."

Eisenhower once said about war, "Plans are useless, but planning is indispensable." Because the fog of war descends when the action starts.

I used to tell corporate executives, particularly in crisis situations, to deal with reality as it is—not as you wish it was. Understanding the reality of a situation is the first step in solving the problem.

Another observation suddenly pops into my mind: *"The best way to succeed is to revel in ambiguity."* Because when the action starts, despite the fog around you, you still have to act—so be decisive when you act. And that is where the planning is so important, because you plan for all the contingencies that you can envision.

Yeah. Where exactly does all this stuff come from?

Random thoughts. How I often occupy my life, it seems.

So, what *would* you say to that ex-girlfriend or boyfriend, that ex-wife or husband, that first love, if you meet them? And more so at a reunion with people who knew you both. The entirety of what you say depends on what you observe when you see her/him, but you must be sure of at least one thing that you want to say—and be sure to say it.

City Slickers pops into my head. Jack Palance schooling Billy Crystal on exactly what is important in life: each of us has to figure it out for ourselves. *City Slickers* is still one of my favorite movies. Like *Stand By Me,* it reflects what men are like—whether they're twelve or

39 or 68, it's all pretty much the same.

What is that one thing you would want her or him to know? I shake my head and try to stop all the thoughts in my head. So I do what we all do when we are alone around other people. I check my phone.

But there is something just on the edge of my consciousness, you know, like when you could swear you heard someone call your name, but there is no one there when you look up. So I look around the room as classmates chatter.

In the doorway is THAT girl ... and she is looking right at me.

CHApter 22

"**S**o, how was it?"

My wife is in bed, reading a book about Sandra Day O'Connor.

"It was fun." I start taking off my clothes. "I talked to more people than I thought I would."

She smiles. She knew.

"And I hugged more people than I have in like a decade."

She smiles. She knew.

"Was Tom there?"

"Yeah," I throw my socks in the closet. "We used each other as a base of operations. We both talked to about a thousand people, told some of the same stories, the same lies."

"Was she there?"

I take off my jeans and put them on the growing pile of clothes on the small table in my walk-in closet. I never hang anything up until the next day.

It first began as an act of corporate rebellion when I shed the uniform at the end of every day, and I have yet to outgrow it in retirement.

"Yes ... she was there."

My wife looks over her reading glasses at me, but otherwise does not move, and keeps her book open so she can start again. "The dog next door?"

I look at my wife. I know she does not really mean it the way it sounds, at least I think that is what I know. Even after more than 46 years together, she is still a mystery.

A missionary, no less, once said to me: "If you think for one minute you have a woman figured out," and he was already laughing, "then you've got it timed just about right."

"Yes, she was there. First time ever to a reunion, I think."

"Did you say everything you wanted to say?"

"Yes, I did."

My wife looks at me and smiles. "Good," is all she says, and she returns to Sandra Day O'Connor.

I get in bed beside her, kiss her goodnight, tell her that I love her, then pull up the covers. "Too tired to read," I say, and I turn out the light that she left on for me.

"I know," she says. And she does.

It is an introvert thing. Extroverts never really understand, even if they say they do. The best an introvert can hope for is acceptance that it really can be hard to talk to people.

As I settle into my side of the bed, I think: if the Sixties really was a time like no other, as so many seem to believe (or maybe many who lived through that time want to hope it was like no other); and if things happened in the Sixties that had never happened before, or since—then it was still a time like any other time.

A time for learning who you are, who you could be, can be … who your real friends are. A time to discover your first love, and what love is—or what it should be—and if you are really lucky, what it can be ….

I remember everything, and I remember the Sixties.

As I close my eyes, I remember something my dad told me. I learned a lot from watching him, but he really didn't *tell* me much except, "be a rebel," for example, and not much else. But when he lay in a hospital bed from which he would never leave, the two of us talked about memories.

We were laughing about something that happened in 1968—a terrible year in the world, but not for us, not for me. As near as I could tell, he never listened to Simon and Garfunkel. But he smiled and looked at me and said, "Preserve your memories, son. They're all that's left you."

I'm pretty sure he's right.

Made in the USA
Monee, IL
07 May 2021